Four week loan

Benthyciad pedair w

Please ... or before the

BOOK

A SHARED JOURNEY THROUGH 'MADNESS'

SHEILA HARVEY, EDITOR AND PART AUTHOR

Published by:
Somerset Virtual College NHS Publications
Dunkirk Memorial House
Minehead Road, Bishops Lydeard
Taunton, Somerset
TA4 3BT
Tel: 01823 431259

A CIP catalogue record for this book
is available from the British Library

ISBN 0-9544475-0-6

Distributed by:
Mind in Taunton and West Somerset
32a North Street
Taunton
Somerset TA1 1LW
01823 334906
Printed by
Taunton Printing Company
Taunton

Somerset Virtual College NHS Publications

With love and gratitude to my family and friends.

With gratitude to, and respect for, my colleagues and those who looked after me professionally.

Finally, I owe a particular debt to all those who have contributed to the book and whose comments continue to shape my experience.

'I can only make direct statements, only "tell stories". Whether or not the stories are "true" is not the problem. The only question is whether what I tell is *my* fable, *my* truth.'

From p.17 of the prologue to 'Memories, Dreams and Reflections' by C.G.Jung, Pub. Collins, The Fontana Library, 1967 edition.

For every copy of the book that is sold, £2.50, a proportion of the price, will go towards the work of

MIND IN TAUNTON AND WEST SOMERSET

LIST OF ILLUSTRATIONS

SHEILA'S BOOK

Contents

Chapters 1-6 are written by Sheila Harvey

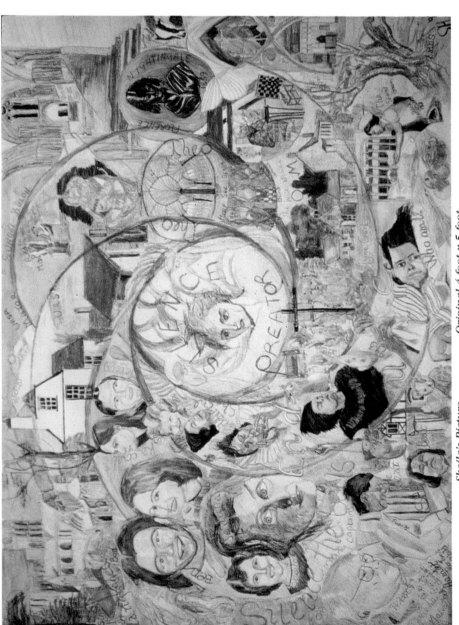

Sheila's Picture   Original 4 foot x 5 foot

FOREWORD BY HARRY PROCTER [1]

There have been numerous books describing a writer's personal journey through madness but none, as far as I know, where the accounts of such a journey by the key people surrounding the writer have been included. This book is deeply moving and fascinating, not only in Sheila Harvey's own profound and terrifying story but because we can read the parallel experiences of members of her family as well as of professionals and others caring for her and visiting her, not knowing whether they would see her emerge from her devastating psychosis.

Since the Second World War, we have come to realize that psychoses are quintessentially *family affairs* in that close relationships can both exacerbate the problems and contribute to the healing of the suffering person. In helping people through serious psychological breakdown, I believe it is crucial to have a deep understanding of the views and experiences of the closest family members as well as those of the sufferers themselves and find how these views relate and interact with each other. In this book, a selection of such views is available allowing the reader to *reconstruct* the drama from a variety of points of view. The pain, the tragedy and the life-and-death struggle of contrary interpretations are here to behold. The book reflects the controversies, raging as strongly as ever, about the nature of major emotional breakdown.

I came to know Sheila initially as my research student when she was studying the effect of panic and anxiety on the breathing difficulties of patients in her chest ward. Her unusually intelligent, penetrating and compassionate qualities were immediately apparent. The supervision process was exciting and exhilarating as Sheila cut great swathes through the theories on offer. Our conversations ranged across many topics from interviewing methods, the role of creativity in the research process through to deep philosophical and psychotherapeutic questions. It is easy to say in hindsight that her exploration of panic was an unconscious presaging or preparation for her own terrifying journey.

The book mirrors in the microcosm of one family perhaps the chief debate in psychology/psychiatry of the age – the role of child sexual abuse in mental health. Over the past twenty years we have now learned far more about how common sexual abuse in the family is, about how devastating its effects are on subsequent development and how paedophiles tend to operate - with grooming, threats and subtle psychological moves to make the child dissociate and forget the transgressions. We also now know that some people are prepared to abuse even infants and that paedophiles sometimes choose to abuse younger children, before continuous memory and language form, in order to get away with it.

The powerful forces invoked by the allegation or disclosure of such abuse, however, has not become any easier to manage. Can one imagine anything that could be seen as more morally reprehensible than the abuse of a helpless and innocent child, especially for the abuser's own sexual gratification? My own experience of working in long term therapy with adult survivors of sexual abuse, as well as with children who disclose current abuse within the family, is testament to how strong the recriminations and denials can be. Permanent rifts in the family are typically created with overwhelming pressure to retract allegations so powerful that the person begins to doubt his or her own experience, or for amnesias and dissociations to form in which people lose contact with whole areas of their own remembered experience.

At a societal level the forces are well documented in what happened to Freud when he argued that sexual abuse or "seduction in childhood" was a factor in the development of hysteria. In *The Assault on Truth*, Jeffrey Masson[2] argues that Freud abandoned his observations and went on to develop psychoanalytic theory, based on the notion that the child *fantasises* sexual contact with the opposite sexed parent. More recently, biological and cognitive-behavioural theories may function in the same way in the argument that emotional disturbance is due to *faulty brain functioning* or irrational thinking. This is not to say that all these phenomena do not occur but the worry is when they are used to deny and disqualify areas of the sufferer's lived experience because it is too complicated or politically inconvenient to be taking them seriously.

These considerations provide a background to the intense dilemmas within Sheila's family. The central problem is though, that we simply *do not know* whether her father did abuse her at the age of three-and-a-half years. In reading Sheila's accounts of her nightmarish hallucinations, being with her during the height of her madness and in long conversations and talks since, I came to believe strongly that the abuse had occurred. But when one reads the heart-rending perspective of her sister Jenifer, who obviously remembers her father with intense love and loyalty, one can be persuaded to the opposite view.

Attempting to reconstruct their father David's experience from the accounts offers a view of an intensely confused and traumatised young man. We know from soldiers returning to society after battle, for instance in writings as recent as the Falklands War, how difficult it is for them to describe to people the contradiction of ghastly and traumatising but also exhilarating and triumphant adventures that they have had. People simply cannot relate to it. The persons may remain silent with their stories untold for the rest of their lives. Men, especially back then, may have a particular difficulty in relating and reflecting on their emotions. David had been working with leprosy and went on to contribute significantly to medical knowledge in this field.

It is easy to empathise with how difficult it must have been for him returning to his family, with a new daughter with whom he had not bonded and with little experience in the way of models and skills in relating to children anyway. For Sheila at that age her father's appearance was experienced as highly threatening and aversive. Her father roared at her, slapped her, was physically repellent in terms of smell, his greasy spotty back…Furthermore his return led to her temporarily losing contact with her mother, as she and Jenifer were sent to be looked after by a neighbour.

Unfortunately none of this really throws light on whether the abuse actually took place as these factors could be used to back hypotheses from both sides of the fence. If the abuse did occur and it was a one-off event, it is likely that it was a different type of phenomenon to the paedophile process described above and to be motivated by anger and rejection rather than sexual gratification.

Sexual abuse by a trusted adult in childhood is a devastating experience because of the intense contradictions it engenders. Here is an adult, my father, who is supposed to protect me, who has power over me, whom I want to love and worship, doing something to me that is harmful, not for my benefit. It may involve unwanted stimulation of erogenous zones, still physically immature, giving rise to intense sensation with a confusing mixture of pleasure and aversion, disgust and pain. At this stage of childhood, construing is still very much in terms of concrete physical features of the world, of self and other as bodies. The child is gradually developing higher order constructs about people such as whether they are happy or not, safe and trustworthy or not and so on, allowing the child to make predictions and learn to behave appropriately within the social rules of the family. Young persons are developing their *identities*, working out *who* they are, *who* others are, about intimacy, hierarchy and boundaries.

Developing a coherent hierarchical construct system is essential for healthy and effective psychological functioning. Sexual abuse and the contradictions involved will be highly disruptive to this process. Working out the contradictions later in adult life may involve a dangerous collapse in this system of constructs, as assumptions about self and others need to be totally re-evaluated.

I believe this is the kind of process that Sheila's psychosis could have comprised; here I am using a Personal Construct Analysis as inspired by the American psychologist, George Kelly[3]. However a *belief* that one has been abused could have exactly the same effect. Either way, helping people through the process involves *validating* and *credulously accepting* their own hypotheses, helping them make sense of their experiences and memories until a new sufficient coherence is achieved in their construing system. The end result, in working with adult survivors, may be a certainty that they were abused, but with very early abuse, the existential certainty that it occurred or not may be impossible to achieve. In this case, coming to terms with the *possibility* that abuse occurred might be the best outcome, leaving the person with intense ambiguity in how to evaluate key figures in their life, including themselves.

I believe the person's internal construct system and the system of construing held by different members of the family are intimately and dynamically related. They reflect each other. Thus when, for example, Jenifer so hotly defends her father with intense loyalty, one can be sure there will be equivalent feelings of loyalty in Sheila's own construing. This is what makes the confrontation with memories (or hallucinations) so painful and guilt provoking. In working in therapy with people, with or without their families, as therapist, I want to be able to support and validate the positions of all members of the family and help them as a group to find a way forward. I have *simultaneously to support positions that are totally contradictory with each other!* Failure to do this may expose the person to the full force of total invalidation and the preventing of re-growth, a process that could be compared initially to nurturing vulnerable seedlings in a hostile environment.

Sheila came through it but perhaps only because of her own deep resilience and bravery and because her family (and key ward staff) provided her with deep love and acceptance. But the power imbalances that can operate in these situations cannot be under-estimated.

Sheila's brother-in-law and second cousin on David's side of the family, Peter, himself a psychiatrist, uses three powerful arguments to back his insistence that their father could not have abused Sheila. Again, no one is to blame him for loyally supporting his father-in-law, but it is the *process* of the argument that I am interested in here. When a child discloses abuse or an adult recovers highly disturbing and traumatic material about childhood abuse, they may be confronted not just by disbelief but by a barrage of reasons why it could not possibly be true. Peter twice mentions David's *reputation*. He uses legal and then psychiatric arguments to back his case.

Recent cases of abuse by professionals, residential social workers and members of the clergy unfortunately do not guarantee that reputation is a necessary safeguard against abuse, which is usually carried out in clandestine privacy, the power relationship itself making disclosure unbelievably difficult. It is precisely because of the abuser's good public reputation that makes disclosure so difficult quite apart from the guilt, shame and self-loathing that sexual abuse engenders.

Secondly, in terms of the legal arguments of the two burdens of proof (the "balance of probabilities" and "beyond reasonable doubt"), of course it is important that people are seen as innocent before being proven guilty and that they are protected from wrongful accusations. But where is the protection in the legal system for the vulnerable where only a tiny proportion of alleged abusers are ever convicted? What protections are built in to the system for ensuring that adult survivors, understandably hugely emotionally insecure and vulnerable because of their experiences, are listened to with the necessary patience and seriousness?

This leads us to Peter's third type of argument, the use of the medical model, which is so worrying in this kind of case. Terms such as "psychotic illness", "delusions", "mood disorders" may be used to disqualify and invalidate peoples' experiences, reducing them to mere brain disorders where all or the convenient parts of peoples' reports are deemed to be meaningless and misleading because "the machinery is not working properly". Again, I am not saying that such phenomena do not exist. In another area of my practice, work with childhood autism, I am the first to argue against those who see autistic spectrum disorders as psychogenic rather than neurodevelopmental disorders. However, within British psychiatry in my experience, there is very little room for allowing for the existence of creative psychological "illnesses" of the type that I believe Sheila may have endured. The medical model still rules as strongly as ever, in spite of moves into the community and the development of partnership with social care. There is hardly any skilled psychotherapeutic help available in the average acute ward. The more serious the disturbance, the more medical thinking predominates and pharmacological treatments exclusively applied. In many teams a very powerful hierarchy exists in which it is very difficult for alternative views to be taken seriously, even by professionals of as high-status as clinical psychologists.

I am not necessarily against the deployment of drug treatments, even in cases of psychological disturbance. It is the *absence* of the opportunity for the person to be helped through a listening, validating and psychotherapeutic stance that is worrying. Even in cases of a purely biological brain disturbance, I believe people should have the chance to talk about and make sense of their disturbing experiences. Strong traditions and old-fashioned training are no doubt to blame. Psychological therapies from these perspectives are seen as too complicated, but may be rejected because they are outside the scope of the existing professionals' skills and interests. However, psychological therapies are not necessarily more complicated and may even be briefer and less expensive as the person and family members are empowered to re-own responsibility and help themselves manage.

Of course, Sheila did recover and went on to write this book. One could therefore argue that the treatment she received was fine and no modifications in it were required. However, as I have said, I fear it was unusual qualities in her and her family, with some particularly helpful staff, that may have prevented the awful possibility of her condition becoming chronic.

1   Harry Procter is Consultant Clinical Psychologist with the Somerset Partnership NHS Trust. His doctoral research looked at interpersonal construing in families of people with psychoses, this forming the basis for an approach to therapy within child and adult mental health. For further details, see: Procter, H.G. (1985) *A Construct Approach to Family Therapy and Systems Intervention*, in Button, E. (ed) *Personal Construct Theory and Mental Health*, Croom Helm, Beckenham, Kent; Procter, H.G. (1987) *Change in the Family Construct System: Therapy of a Mute and Withdrawn Schizophrenic Patient*. In Neimeyer, R. and Neimeyer, G. (eds) Personal Construct Therapy Casebook, Springer Publications, New York and Procter, H.G. & Pieczora, R. (1992) *A Family Oriented Community Mental Health Centre*. In Treacher, A. & Carpenter, J. (eds) Using Family Therapy in the 90's. Blackwell, Oxford.

2   Masson, J. M. (1992) *The Assault on Truth: Freud and Child Sexual Abuse*. Fontana, London.

3   Kelly, G. A. (1955) A Theory of Personality - the Psychology of Personal Constructs, New York: Norton.

SHEILA'S BOOK

1. THE LADY OF SHALOTT

January 14th, 1997. There's something about 1997 - I keep wanting to write 1977. What was I doing then? Twenty years ago I was 34 and the children were eight, seven, and five. We were living in North Hertfordshire, in a rural village, a large one - almost a town. Jeremy was teaching at the local comprehensive and was the Deputy Head Master there while I had just returned to nursing, or would soon do so. We had moved to Hertfordshire from Dorset three years earlier and it had been a sea change for us, from the private sector of education to the public, from a protected independent school environment to an ordinary community where friends had to be found. I felt exposed and vulnerable but also ready for the change. The primary school where the children all went had proved a good place to make friends and it didn't take long for people of similar interests to meet.

My book will evolve in different ways but a diary structure might be as useful a way to begin as any. Dipping in and out of time and seeing where the present takes the story. The beginning of a new year is a good time for me, just as Christmas tends to be a low one, however smoothly arrangements go and however blessed one might be with the presence of family. Last night held a wide-awake period with creative ideas forming. I had finished a large therapeutic painting/drawing just before the 'children' returned for Christmas. I'd been working on it for nearly three years from its first conception after my discharge from the local psychiatric hospital. I'd been an inpatient there for most of the period between May and October 1993, with a very difficult month at home during August. The picture was, is, an attempt to capture the hallucinatory visions; to try and piece together; to remember and to increase my sense of control and understanding. I found that as I concentrated on recreating a face, or a place or thinking about where the subject should be placed, or how the whole should be unified, insights would rise to the surface of the mind and could be held: a little more understanding achieved. It's a big picture and I'm no artist. At school one of the few times I enjoyed was in the art class, but as an adult, apart from a bit of sketching, nothing, until Jeremy and I joined a local group on a Saturday morning to develop our drawing and painting skills.

Early on in that process I'd attempted a self-portrait combined with a painting of Jeremy to give to Ben our son, for his 21st birthday. I had never looked so closely at my face before, never really looked into my own eyes. I made myself vulnerable in the process and recognised the pain there as never before. When he saw the painting Ben laughed and said it was nothing like me, but I thought otherwise. His 21st birthday was on May 16th 1993; by the end of that month I was in the process of an 'acute psychotic breakdown'. There had been few warning signs and I'm fairly certain none that others had perceived.

January 15th 1997, Wednesday. It occurred to me after writing yesterday that Tennyson's lines from 'The Lady of Shalott' - 'the mirror cracked from side to side, the curse has come upon me cried the Lady of Shalott' - had some imaginative reflections to offer. She knew that if she looked out of the window the curse would be realised: that is, if she looked beyond the immediate four walls of her room to the outside world, or in psychological language beyond the defended self, to the beauty and abyss beyond. The temptation for her was the vision of Sir Lancelot riding into the frame of the mirror and the cost of looking at reality was death. The curse in my terms could be seen as the 'repressed' and therefore forgotten past. In looking closely at myself and particularly the expression in my eyes, at last I was facing the reality and it led to the river and thence to the seas of unconsciousness. But I am alive and need no requiem lament.

Jo rang last night. She was feeling totally inadequate in her new role as a primary school teacher. She is now 26 and has really had to fight hard to qualify for the work. It was her original aim. She's very good with children and has always enjoyed their company. She took time to collect the necessary A levels. After a few temporary jobs and false starts she got an HND at Southampton Institute and then moved on to College, to read English. While there she achieved both her English/Drama degree and passed her Maths at the required level. This enabled her to stay put and do her Post Graduate Certificate of Education. By July last year she was looking for a teaching post. Jo has always needed a secure home base. By this time she'd met David, also a Graduate from her college and they had decided to live together. Her next priority was to find and settle into a flat in Worcester with him. She missed the boat for permanent jobs in September and had been doing supply work until the present job came up. This one is covering someone's maternity leave. So Jo is still in the business of looking for a permanent post for September this year.

When she rang last night I did my best to boost her morale. She commented that I sounded very calm and it occurred to me that I was perhaps exercising a kind of hypnosis through the tone of my voice, in an attempt to stop her panicking. I suggested she did an hour's work - just make a start - and that I'd ring back. She was much better by then and this evening when I rang had survived the day and made some helpful decisions. David has been doing a good support job. Jo is a lovely person and is shown along with all the family in my picture. She was doing her degree; I think it would have been the end of her first year, when I was ill. In her long vacation she came home to give Rachel a break.

Rachel, our eldest child, 15 months older than Jo, had been there throughout the crisis and when I was admitted had been at home. She took on the task of housekeeping for Jeremy and generally helping to hold things together as well as visiting me regularly in hospital. Jo over this time proved a quiet, calming influence. David stayed for a period and never made me feel that my illness upset or worried him. When I shook with uncontrollable tension Jo was able to pick up my hands and, through instinctive touch, draw the shaking out through my fingertips. I reverted to calling her a baby name 'Doey' or rather pronouncing Jo in a baby way, all part of a profound regression on my part, but it expressed a child-like playfulness. Much of this time I was in a 51 year old's body with a mind swinging between adult knowledge and powers of endurance on the one hand to the infant in part, and the three and a half year old Sheila (at that age and later the family called me She or She-She) on the other.

January 16th, Thursday. A hard day's work followed by a food shop, so finally sat down about 9 pm when J got back earlier than expected. The Governors have accepted his resignation with suitable expressions of regret. He's been Head of one of the local comprehensives for the last 19 years and for the last term or two has been the longest serving Secondary Head, and the oldest, at 58, I think. Now he's got to write a suitable letter for the parents and by tomorrow evening it will be public knowledge. Until the beginning of this term we'd been thinking that another couple of years would be about right, with retirement at 60. He had flu over Christmas and the start of term required a lot of effort, unusual for him. The Chief Education Officer (CEO) came to make sure that he was aware of the Government's stand that after the end of March teachers couldn't opt to retire before 60. He was aware of it of course and had been talking to his own staff where it affected them. Suddenly he realised that no, he didn't want to struggle on. There are so many things he wants to do and achieve still, apart from the school - writing, art, sport, Church commitments and so forth. The CEO assured him that there was no question of giving him a gentle shove and J believed him! Anyway it looks as though the end of March it is - very close now. Financially we'll have to do a lot of adjusting. Unexpectedly I also felt a great relief - odd, as I've been more concerned about financial security in our retirement up till now and thought we needed another two years. We must both have been carrying a bigger burden than we realised, mine has been merely support and there have been many times when I didn't want to hear another word about education.

To revert to The Lady of Shalott, I've now read it again and found several more points of interest. This lady is an unknown quantity - 'Or is she known in all the land?'; hearing her song the reaper, piling sheaves in the moonlight, describes her as 'the fairy Lady of Shalott', and the web she weaves is magic. Then completing the circle 'She has heard a whisper say, A curse is on her if she stay To look down to Camelot. She knows not what the curse may be, And so she weaveth steadily..........' The enchantment or curse is not simply laid on her, she herself is a fairy able to weave a magic web, an idealised world and for a time she is content enough. She does not seek to know the extent or nature of the curse until finally she becomes 'half sick of shadows' and emotionally vulnerable to the image of Sir Lancelot. I'd forgotten that once she looked down on him and the curse broke Tennyson has the line 'Out flew the web and floated wide', her creation is destroyed. Between parts three and four the season seems to have moved from summer to autumn and of course the mood from brightness to gloom. The point of all this for myself is the parallel movement of the psyche, from semi-content and denial to dissatisfaction and action towards discovering once and for all what the sense of oppression/depression/unreality is about. The timescale starts with the sense of the normal, easy passage of time but once the action is forced suddenly a season has passed and the Lady is finding her boat-hearse. Nobody helps her: she is utterly on her own and throughout the poem there has been no hint of any servants or companions; this is indeed a fairy isle, the Island of Shalott.

Water is ever- present in images of the unconscious. In this poem the magic isle is surrounded by water. The final journey to death is made on it. When I dream of rising rivers, of sea tides rising and trapping me, there is always a nightmare quality and a sense of relief when I awake. Now that I take dreams and their content seriously I turn round, look at my waking life and feel a certain anxiety about repetitions. The best way I can describe the recovery process from the acute phase of the illness is by saying that the feeling of being haunted, of being permanently full of dread, of being threatened by too much purposeless, unhappy time ahead, have been replaced by feelings of safety, of assurance, of the capacity for joy and the prospect of time with lots of creative and happy things to do.

The sea rises   *Wells Cathedral*   *Home*

My parents in later life *Pan*

2. PAN

January 20th 1997 Monday. Well J's proposed retirement is now established fact and all the necessary people know. It's good to be able to talk freely about it. At the weekend Derek and Mia came to stay, old friends from Hertfordshire days. Derek has retired from a senior sales management post with one of the big drug companies. Mia has done various things since their two daughters grew up enough to give her some independence. The present career development is as a consultant in garden design after she attended a course in London. Mia is Finnish and carries with her that artistic sense which I associate with her country. We asked her to redesign our garden when her course had ended. The process has been fascinating, expensive (the actual doing of it), and the laying down just completed. Stage 1 was completed in the late summer of 1995 and stage 2 just a few weeks ago. The spring promises to be particularly exciting with the bulbs coming through for the second year together with the new ones just planted and all sorts of new plants waiting to burgeon. Mia hadn't yet seen the realisation of her plan and she was pleased with what she saw.

With these two, memories of the years from 1974 to 1978 are replayed and all the years since, as we've kept in touch. Our children are the same age and Jo and Katriina, Mia and Derek's younger daughter, have always got on well, though they only contact one another now and again. The move to Hertfordshire frightened me, it was also stimulating - a new phase. The fear arose from the fact that for the first seven years of married life we had lived in Dorset where Jeremy was an assistant master at a boys' school. It was a closed, comfortable, narrow-minded community. We lived mostly in school properties apart from a couple of years in a flat which we rented from a member of staff. It is a beautiful small town, built largely in ham stone, with many old buildings. It's set in lovely countryside. It became clear towards the end of our time there that J was unlikely to be promoted within the school so we decided to cut our losses and look elsewhere. He started applying for jobs within the state sector and landed the deputy headship of a small, new comprehensive school in Hertfordshire. Rachel had spent just one term at primary school when we moved at the end of the Spring term of 1974. We left behind some good friends and of course the family had been born in Sherborne. For me it had been a time of adjusting to marriage, to a change; then a giving up of a job, and then to three pregnancies within three and a half years with all the mothering that entailed. I was very unsure of myself both as a wife and a mother.

The fear which I felt was about the move into the 'real world'. We were buying our own property for the first time, had no ready community to move into, did not know Hertfordshire, at least not this bit of it and there was the challenge of the job for J. We spent just four years there. At the end of this time I was surer of myself in many respects, much more secure with Jeremy and although my own parents and siblings did not view me as the maternal type, the children nevertheless thrived. I learned to love the rolling arable fields and small villages of this area. Cambridge was not far away. A city where we had already spent a Sabbatical Easter term, with Rachel aged between nine months and a year and Jo due the following July. It was good to be near it again.

January 25th 1997 Saturday. This morning we joined our fortnightly art group as usual. It's not a class. Tom and Pat Preater paint and encourage a few of us to join them. Tom is primarily a sculptor and has done a couple of carvings for us. Each piece has a particular significance and has been drawn into my picture. My sister Jenifer and brother-in-law/second cousin, Peter, had given us two small pieces of Carrara marble on their return from Italy. They knew we were interested in sculpture at the time. One piece was about a foot high, the other maybe two. For some years they had sat outside in our several gardens waiting for the right moment and person to carve them.

At some point after our move to Taunton we met Tom and became familiar with his work. He carved the Stations of the Cross for St. George's, Taunton. These are virtually full size and very powerful, original works of art. We asked Tom to carve a figure of Pan for us out of the smaller piece of marble. In June, 1988, as a birthday present for me from J, Tom delivered him to the house. A few days later I wrote about the process of realising Pan as an important image for me; about the possibility of getting him sculpted and then a description of the actual carving and the final figure. I have included this here. Looking back Pan seems to have represented some of the feelings that were surfacing about my father. He's an ambivalent figure both in terms of what he represents and in the feelings which he evokes in me and 'he' can apply there equally well to them both.

" A gradual dawning in my consciousness of this pagan god and, like most beginnings, it cannot be accurately dated. It can be confidently stated however that two blocks of Carrara marble were brought back by my sister and brother-in law from Italy and given to us. We were intrigued by sculpture, even to the extent of trying the art/craft ourselves. Discouragment soon set in, despite using easier materials, and the stones stood as small menhirs in the garden for some years. It was much later that we learned that marble is softer and easier to work when freshly cut from the quarry. We also learned that Michelangelo frequently had blocks of it standing for long

periods of time in his studio before setting to work on them. Carrara marble carries this aura: that it is the stone which was his chosen medium: it is special: So we looked at the stones and when we moved house they moved house, or rather garden, with us.

I had seen a friend's Pan figure set in her garden and it had pleased me. It was a good statue, appropriately set, half hidden in climbing greenery, secret, surprising. He pushed his way further towards the daylight of my awareness. There were other earlier reminders. One of the local vicars, with a small, neat physique and a pointed beard also enjoys the Pan myth and when dressed up as the god could almost pass as 'real'. Later he was to lend us recordings made on pipes which are said to replicate Pan's. I had reread 'The Wind in the Willows' and found Kenneth Graham's description in the chapter entitled 'Piper at the Gates of Dawn'. It verges on the sentimental and shows a single facet of Pan's nature, but it is an effective piece of writing.

Versions of the myth vary. Pan was said to be so ugly that his mother rejected him - but wherein lay his ugliness? Was it in the goat/man form; in the great phallus which some versions say he possessed (leading to his identification with Priapus); or perhaps in the actual features of his face?

As god of the fields and woods he cared for the herds and flocks, making them fertile; for bees and their honey and for vines with their grape harvest. He is linked with Arcadia most strongly but appears with different characteristics throughout the Mediterranean. There is a twist to Pan's myth, that on the birth of Christ a great shout was heard by a sailor 'Pan is dead', and, so the story goes, the gods died with him. In refutation of this it is suggested that the shout heard was more likely to be linked with the annual grieving rituals for the death of Adonis. Today we are told 'God is dead'. Consciousness is an ever evolving phenomena. No doubt both the gods, Pan and God Himself, are very much alive in the being of individuals and nations.

A local sculptor, Tom, carves mainly in wood. He has created great church figures, amongst them the Stations of the Cross for St George's Church. They breath life and death. Getting to know him and his work we wondered if he would carve in stone and in marble in particular. More particularly would he carve a Pan for me? Tom agreed and as we talked the Pan myth; as I shared my idea of Pan I knew that the sculptor's skill and imagination must be free and that I had to accept the Pan who emerged whether he satisfied me or not; that perhaps I was searching for the impossible. It was an exciting prospect.

The hope was that he would be completed for June as a birthday present for me from J - not to mention Tom. On two or three occasions we shared the creative process, first looking at some preliminary drawings of Tom's , then at the emerging form from the stone. In the early drawing the features were too ugly, too monkey-like. 'It's not that he should be beautiful - but wouldn't he have at least an ugly attraction?' Tom was receptive to other ideas, seeming to seek for a truth outside us both. Then great curving horns, where I had visualised short stumpy ones, here Tom convinced me how right his own concept was. Certainly Pan proved harder work than Tom had foreseen, the marble giving only slowly and the working of the final polish requiring long minutes/hours of love and patience. The high polish he placed in small areas - brow, nose, cheeks, arms, hands and part of the back, while horns and hair were left rougher with glyph marks following the flow. The lower legs and cloven hoofs were again polished.

I saw none of this later work until Tom brought him up on the day, together with his chain-saw to reduce a trunk of medlar wood to a plinth at the right height for the sculpture. The medlar had died in my mother's garden and it felt good to find other uses for it.

Apart from family, we had invited three close friends to be present on the occasion, the Pan-erection. Tom arrived before them. I felt nervous and, no doubt, he did too. Pan was lifted out of the car and placed on the low wall dividing the courtyard from the rest of the garden. There he sat, cross-legged, head thrown back, eyes closed, totally absorbed in the music he was creating on his pipes; a compact figure, perhaps fifteen inches high and eight inches across at his widest point; his curved horns whorled and curling round again at the tips into his scalp at the base of the skull; the hair was suggested by a stippled effect; his ears slightly pointed; his face primitive yet also aesthetic in its curves and strong cheek bones; from his chin a growth of beard covered by the pipes, held by strong, capable hands to his lips; the line of the forearms to the elbows making me perceive the beauty in it for the first time, and up to powerful shoulders through to the curve of the neck where it met with the beard line. Below his beard abdominal muscles met at the umbilicus and led down to more hair and a clearly but unobtrusively delineated penis - on either side strong thighs where his elbows rested on the crooked knees and again below the knee a flow of hair leading into foreleg and cloven hoof.

I had to see him from all angles and his back is striped with darker marble as if bruised, (and Pan was surely bruised in spirit?) behind the marble marking the anatomy of the back, tilted down to his left where his right hand is held higher up the pipe with his head slightly to the left. Tom had already pointed out that he is a study in triangles and from this view there is the triangle of his horns, of the breadth of his shoulders down to a narrow waist and hip line. His buttocks disappear into a flow of hair and grass. At his sides emerging from his shoulders down past his armpits are further shags of hair. One more turn to look at his left side, and further triangles; of the pan-pipes; of his bent arm and crossed knee. The hands, meeting across the pipes with the tip of the left fingers just overlapping the right, suggest a sensitivity not noticed before. The clean cut of the cloven hoof is very apparent now. Curiously the marble markings could be the marks of a whip lash - although belied by the tranquillity of his face. I remember that when the hunt was unsuccessful images of Pan would be whipped 'by way of reprisal'.

How can one convey how completely satisfying this figure is, how he will feed my soul? It is not only sight that is satisfied, but touch - he is wonderful to touch - from smooth to rough, over his muscles and down his hair, round his horns - and Pan likes to be touched, there is no offence, no sense of sacrilege.

Somehow Tom has expressed in form, a universal aspect of our natures. How else could he represent something so perfectly for me when we do not know each other well? We have met half a dozen times and my response to him has been one of instinctive trust and liking, with a great respect for his craft, but there is no conscious knowledge of each other's minds or souls. The communication has to be on the unconscious, universal level. What can be said is that we did talk truth to each other over Pan. In creating Pan, Tom is enabling me to become more whole.

There is more to be thought about. Pan's pipes are explained by the story that he was attracted by the beauty of the nymph Syrinx and was pursuing her 'when she begged her father - the river god Ladon - to turn her into a reed', this he did. Pan frustrated, bending over the reeds caught the sound they made in response to his breath. He cut them and fashioned his pipes, learning to play them with great beauty. One imagines a wild, melancholy sound. The pipes become Pan's way of expressing his loss. The move is one from the simple satisfaction of desire to its frustration and from the frustration is born an art of great beauty which uplifts and attracts those who hear it.

This is a neat illustration of Keats' theory which I've discovered by chance and from Pan. Looking at Pan, Keats' lines came to mind:-

'A thing of beauty is a joy for ever,
Its loveliness increases; it will never
Pass into nothingness; but still will keep
A bower quiet for us, and a sleep
Full of sweet dreams, and health, and quiet breathing.
Therefore, on every morrow, are we wreathing
A flowery band to bind us to the earth,
Spite of despondence, of the inhuman dearth
Of noble natures.........'

Needing to check the accuracy of my version, I found a book of his poems and discovered that these lines are only the opening few in his much longer

Pan

Sculptor: Tom Preater

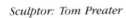

poem Endymion. I must have found them in an anthology and never looked for the source. I read on and found a wonderful creation of poetic Arcady. It dawned on me that this was a description of Pan's country and as the lines moved on to describe a religious ceremony, it seemed deeply felicitous that the ceremony was in honour of Pan - and five long verses a hymn of praise to him. To quote several extracts:-

'Strange ministrant of undescribed sounds,
That come a-swooning over hollow grounds,
And wither drearily on barren moors:
Dread opener of the mysterious doors
Leading to universal knowledge'

And again:-

'Be still the unimaginable lodge
For solitary thinkings; such as dodge
Conception to the very bourne of heaven,
Then leave the naked brain: be still the leaven
That spreading in this dull and clodded earth,
Gives it a touch ethereal - a new birth:
Be still a symbol of immensity;
A firmament reflected in a sea;
An element filling the space between;
An unknown - but no more......'

I turned back to the introduction and read this quotation from a letter of Keats. 'Do you not see, how necessary a world of pains and troubles is to school an intelligence and make it a soul?' and the comment which followed 'This philosophy of soul-making differs, as Keats was at pains to point out, from the Christian belief which he felt too narrow, in that we start not with a soul but with an intelligence, as he calls it. The troubles of the world help this intelligence to become a soul'.

Discussing this later with Maggie, she believes that the soul exists from the point of conception. This has to be a matter of faith, which at present has no reality for me. Then there is the broad-minded vision that all great truths eventually meet at the source of 'All Truth' - but I ask why should they? I rather hold an image of these insights and expressions of meaning as running parallel. For each person who can own insight into one or more, so much the richer is that person. But do they lead anywhere? The whole idea of travel to a point may be an irrelevance - there is only, as T.S.Eliot has said in so many ways, the present and what we bring to it."

February 1st 1997 Saturday. I've said enough about Pan but I just want to bring him up to date. Originally the intention had been to have him outside but he was too precious so he's been in ever since. With our newly-designed garden there is an ideal spot for him on a pedestal in a circle of bricks. We decided to have Pan cloned and to produce two epoxy-resin versions, one for Tom and one for ourselves. The process was not without its excitements. When we went to pick up the two clones and our original Pan, our Craftsman/Sculptor had forgotten to put the screw in the base. We needed this to ensure that we could secure him onto the pedestal. Nothing daunted he tipped one of the clones on his face and took his cordless drill to his under-parts. Watching I had a premonition that this was not the way to treat even an image of an image of a god. Sure enough as I lifted the 'screwed' clone across the well at the back of the car he split cleanly down the middle. There was no argument about a replacement. We finally got our copy a couple of weeks later. He looks as if he's always been sitting in just that spot of the garden and is of a suitably bronze-like colour. So June 1988 saw our marble Pan instated in the house and autumn 1996 his bronze-like copy in the garden. The source of my information about Pan has been Robert Graves' 'The Greek Myths', in the Folio edition.

3. MEMORY IN 'MADNESS' -REPRESSED OR FALSE?

February 25th 1997 Tuesday
Spent the morning and early afternoon in my role of Lay Assessor for the Social
Services, inspecting rehabilitation homes for those getting over, or learning to
live with some kind of mental distress. I go in to look at the homes from the
residents' point of view and to be an independent person to whom they can
talk if they want to. It felt like a useful contribution. Still had to get to work as
I had a course to prepare for tomorrow – one that I've not done before. The
week before last was half-term, Jeremy's last as a head-teacher. It proved to be a
period of time which had a quality all of its own. The first weekend we spent
at home. It was mild and we did quite a lot in the garden, weeding and putting
compost down, moving the odd plant and enjoying the sight of bulbs emerging.
On Monday I had to carry out an inspection in the morning, after lunch we
caught the coach up to London and spent a couple of nights with Jenifer and
Peter, my sister and brother-in-law - lots of walking, art galleries and a theatre on
Tuesday evening where we saw 'Art' and enjoyed it, while thinking it had been
hyped over its true worth. On Wednesday we looked at Howard Hodgkin's art
at the Hayward. Jeremy was very excited by it. I was more interested in the
Prinzhorn Collection in the upper gallery. This is a collection of art created by
psychotic patients in Germany in the early part of the century. Prinzhorn was
the psychiatrist who understood the therapeutic and diagnostic value of this
kind of work. He put the collection together between 1919 and 1922. His job
was taken over by someone approved of by the Nazis and several of the artists
whose works were represented, were exterminated by them - a bleak and
indigestible bit of history. Most of the art was extremely detailed, with elaborate,
small writing and evidence of complex, inaccessible, systems of thought. It
looked very different from the pictures emerging from the art therapy scene in
this country today. It would be interesting to talk to an art therapist about the
way in which psychotic art reflects the current time; the social setting; the
individual artist and how far it tends to be archetypal.

In the National Portrait Gallery the previous day I'd seen the original bust of
Florence Nightingale, which is in my own painting. The painting was based on a
photograph of it in a Nursing History, but I hadn't, until now, seen the original
or appreciated that it's housed there.

At the end of the week we went to Bristol and took part in a conference - a trialogue between the psychodynamic, spiritual and literary disciplines. We had all read a book by Derek Henson 'Lunch with Mussolini'. It was chosen not because it's great literature but because none of the literati present were likely to have subjected it to academic scrutiny and because it covers important issues. It also infuriated enough of us to prove a very good basis for discussion. The value in the weekend for me was the debate around whom story/history belongs to. Is there such a thing as a 'true' version? I related the debate to my own attempt to write about my experience of psychosis. At one level it will be my story, my truth, but stories also change through time and memories are not necessarily facts. There has been a lot of concern recently about the 'False Memory Syndrome' theory. No one person can be absolutely certain that recovered memory is the recovery of something that actually happened unless there is enough corroborative evidence. People will differ in their view of acceptable evidence, especially when dealing with the infantile world of psychodynamics. Is psychosis an individual, social or family phenomenon - or all three? Is it rooted in our genetics? Is it an illness in the medical sense?

The debate around 'story' confirmed my belief that my book has to approach the experience from as many family, friends' and professional viewpoints as practicable. There will be no need for suppression or for being made dumb.

Pat, my psychotherapist, was also there that weekend. It was good to see her. I was concerned that we'd have to play the conventional therapist/client roles. Whilst these have been both necessary and helpful in the past they no longer felt appropriate. Pat moved our relationship on to an easy friendship and it's clear to us both that the psychotherapy is over. Were I ever to need this kind of help again it would make sense to seek it near to home. The journey to Pat takes an hour and a half. At the time I became acutely ill I was no longer seeing her regularly - if I remember rightly only about once in six months.

October 12th 2002 Saturday

Jenifer's account, in Chapter 11, will provide a very healthy balance to my disturbed one below, which follows in 'Sheila's letter to Sheila'. It was written five years ago after a preliminary debate with Jenifer and Peter, my sister and brother-in-law. What I am writing now has emerged from a further deep conversation with them and Jeremy the other day. Peter's contribution comes later on in the book and reflects a valid alternative explanation to mine, which is the fruit of his psychiatric and therapeutic experience over many years. In the intervening years the subject has been avoided, we all hoped time would resolve the impasse between us. With the imminent likelihood of the book being printed, I sent them a copy as it stood and made it clear that they were free to respond. The time in which they could do this was curtailed, which affronted Peter's normal approach to writing, which is both academic, exact and takes him time.

Wells' Chapter House   The three wise monkeys   Tom Preater

Our usual family relationships are affectionate and happy. We enjoy many shared memories and common interests. Jenifer is my closest living relative, in both age and in the emotional and geographical sense, apart that is, from my own family. None of us want this to be sacrificed for the sake of an uncertain memory. Equally knowing that I have remained convinced of the reality of my recovered memory over the nine years since the psychotic episode and that it remained the lynch pin of my understanding as to the major cause of this anguished period, they were worried that their confrontation would cause me further breakdown or disintegration.

We came to our meeting deeply concerned to find an honest way through. I was not willing to compromise my own experience and integrity. I was prepared to write under a pseudonym and to alter names in the book as appropriate. In the event this has proved unnecessary. The week leading up to this time had been a time of anguish and a testing of the present strength of my psyche. It has remained as well as it has ever been, under this pressure.

During the evening I listened to Peter's exposition on the nature of delusions in particular. He emphasised the fact that the 'memory' was experienced in a time when my mind was doing many extraordinary things, when it was at fever pitch. Although I had ordinary memories before this time of a father who smacked me as a child, of whom I was afraid and who in my late teens had behaved oddly (but with no sexual touch involved) towards me, I was already in a deepening psychotic state before I remembered the episode described in my letter to myself below.

As Peter talked and helped me to see that delusions may not just be ideas, but may be accompanied by physical sensation, I realised that I had no grounds for certainty that such an event had ever actually taken place. If so I would be doing my father a grave (in both senses) injustice were I to sound convinced in this book that it had actually happened. Other delusions and/or hallucinations that I had experienced had been more easily recovered from. For example I 'knew' that I was going to die imminently. Obviously as I got better I knew that I was alive and well and that that total conviction was wrong. Another example was my hallucinatory experience of being crucified and killed in a number of horrible and painful ways. When I recovered I knew that to be an hallucination. This had never happened to me. What was 'interesting' about this one though was that I literally felt the pain, saw the scene, smelt, heard and tasted. The fact that my experience of oral abuse in the psychosis seemed to be an actual memory because I was seeing it, smelling it, feeling it, does not put it, necessarily, in a different category from the crucifixion experience. The problem with my 'recovered memory' is that as I got better I had no external reality against which to test it. There is no evidence (excepting Jenifer's memory), it is too long ago and my parents are dead. The memory can be understood as metaphor but not taken literally. As you read the following, remember I am talking of my own experience. For many people recovered memory can be shown to have a basis in fact. We know that there is a shocking amount of abuse in the world.

The second area, which needs to be emphasised at this point, is the degree of stress that I was experiencing at the time. Peter has summarised these in Chapter 12 and there is no need to repeat these here. They have been partially alluded to in my other chapters and in the family contributions. However, it needs to be said that I was deeply concerned about family issues affecting Jeremy, myself and our three children, which will not be spelt out due to the others' right to confidentiality. There was probably quite enough exceptional stress at the time to cause the breakdown. My understanding is that the stresses sapped me of the energy I needed to cope with both my present and my past.

I am not making any kind of political statement, only telling my story and my truth as it seemed to me. Nor am I entering on either side of a fierce academic debate. So this is the account which I wrote and it needs to be read alongside Jenifer's in Chapter 11.

November 11th 1997 Sunday

I've been trying to write about what I believe to be the cause of the psychosis and have found it easiest to write it in the form of a letter to myself. It goes as follows: -

Dear Sheila

Just start writing about this memory - the memory that you repressed, which you had no way of understanding, let alone allowing yourself to feel. You were only three and a half, a lively, pretty, intelligent and naughty child. You lived with your mother and elder sister, who would have been five and a half, exactly two years older. Since your birth this had been your family unit although the first year or so had been spent with cousins, when your mother had gone to live with her elder sister who had three children then, the youngest a baby a few months younger than you.

It was not an easy arrangement and your mother found a cottage to rent in the Hertfordshire countryside. It stood opposite the big house where the owner lived.

The men had been absent. Your father had been a prisoner of the Japanese in the Far East for the last three and a half years, a little longer than you had been alive. Your mother had been carrying you when she escaped from Singapore - the men stayed behind. Now the war was over, 1945, and the stranger whom you knew only from a photograph, had returned. Dark, bearded and emaciated, yet still to a small child powerful, dominant and frightening. You did not like him, nor did he like you, you suspect.

To give your parents some time alone together you and your sister went to stay with the people over in the big house, the daughter was in her teens and was a friend who played with you both. You went for walks and saw your mother and father in the garden of the cottage and while your mother waved and smiled, you were not allowed to be with her - remember? Remember the pain? The bewilderment? The wire fence dividing you? The hatred of this man who was coming between you and the person whom you loved most? How long was that holiday for? Possibly for a week or a fortnight and then the four of you would have been together. How could you at that age understand your parents' need to be alone together; their need to begin to heal the hurt of your father's imprisonment; to begin to re-establish their relationship?

Your mother had had enough of the responsibility of keeping the family going; of making ends meet; of keeping her grief private and of trying to make you behave. Until recently she had no way of knowing for sure if her much loved husband was alive or dead. Three scrappy postcards in three and a half years were all that she had to go on. Now perhaps she hoped that some of the burden would be taken over, for a few months at least. She made your father responsible for disciplining you when you went beyond limits. Your father's limits were extremely narrow. Whatever he had been like before the war, from the time he returned he was intolerant of children, especially those closest to him. You had to be very good indeed, and of course you weren't, you hated him, you hated the turmoil and change that his return had brought.

So it was that you would be naughty and he would punish you by smacking you. You've always remembered that. You've always remembered the fear; the time you escaped by climbing out of the upstairs window and sliding down the porch roof. Maybe you also tried to hide by clinging onto the cot springs from underneath? Certainly in the episode of your madness in your early fifties they had to take the bed away and leave your mattress on the floor because you spent time underneath the bed clinging to the springs - terrified - hiding.

During the time of this madness, in 1993, you believe you remembered things that you had repressed into forgetfulness. You remembered a dark room, the physical presence, the force against your shoulders – the 'thing' in your mouth –pain, revulsion, terror: blackness, heat, pressure. Did it happen once? Several times? (When you are asked for evidence, when you feel the total disbelief of your sister and brother-in-law/second cousin you feel confused and hurt and wonder what standards of truth and objective reality can possibly be brought to a repressed memory of over fifty years ago?) You must be dumb, never, on any account tell anyone. How could you tell what you had no words for? You would be into your forties before child abuse became an acknowledged, shocking fact of our society. Until then there was no framework within which the memory could make any kind of sense. Consciously you had set your parents up as gods. It was only by believing absolutely in them that you could endure what was happening to you in the years after this period when you were away at boarding school. Here there

The stairs of the Chapter House *Florence Nightingale*

was no emotional warmth, no holding, no deep caring, no home to go to each day, no 'present' parent, you were just one among many. When you were with your parents it was as if you all played at 'happy families', you had no idea how to be with each other and you never felt you knew them at anything other than the superficial level.

You sucked both your index fingers; probably from the time your mother weaned you. At some point, while still at the English cottage, you dropped the centre of the hot plate on your right hand, burning your finger so you gave it up in favour of your left index finger. The habit was to stay with you until you were twelve or thirteen. The photographs, which were taken in the period when you were unable to communicate rationally, show your left hand fingers around your open mouth. This photograph has been used in the drawing. You believe the finger sucking to be a non-verbal communication in a period of profound regression, just as the original habit was maintained in the first place. Your front teeth were pushed out and, despite many plates and numerous visits to the dentist, stayed out until you gave up sucking. You also squinted and wore pink round-rimmed National Health spectacles from the age of 4 until you were 14. Your parents had a horror of saying anything that might make their children 'big-headed'. As a result, in your early teens, you thought of yourself as unattractive. You had no self-confidence.

When you were an in-patient at the local mental hospital, you were eating very little, sleeping badly despite heavy sedation and in the month during which they let you go home, (only to be readmitted), you were panicking at meal times, absenting yourself while you regurgitated, and retched. This behaviour was expressed in someone who normally enjoys her food. It was regressive and, you now believe, associated with memories of oral abuse. In the end you went back to hospital for another three months.

How did your father come to terms with this, if at all? You don't know what he said to your mother: what he indicated. So many men who returned after the war were uncared for; being brave; trying to cope; debilitated and disorientated after years of loss of power. There was no counselling available even had the need been recognised. Your father was probably appalled at what he'd done and hated both himself and you for it. It would colour the rest of his life and your own; making a normal, happy relationship between the two of you impossible.

Of course you saw very little of him. I don't know what your mother knew or guessed but she was determined to keep her family together and now she herself was pregnant again. At some point a Belgian girl, presumably around the age of 18, came and joined the family. You have stayed in touch and remain very fond of her. It was before your father returned to the Far East and before the first of your two younger brothers was born. She must have stayed with you until the family went to join your father, six months after the birth. Your mother's unmarried twin sister went out with you and was to live with the family during school holidays, until she herself got married. From some time after your father's return and before the baby's birth, there was always another woman in the house (until, at the age of eight, you were sent back to school in England and your aunt got married).

No sooner were you out there than you were sent to boarding school, with your sister, seventy miles to the north of your home and the base of your father's work. He was a medical superintendent. Your aunt was also up at the school where she had been appointed as the games' mistress. This arrangement meant that your mother only saw her daughters in the school holidays and it began when you were still not five. When your own eldest daughter reached that age you knew how it would have torn you apart had you had to send her away to boarding school. You asked yourself whether it had really been so impossible to keep a five year old at home and teach her the rudiments of the three Rs yourself. There was plenty of domestic help at that time. Now you believe she thought you were safer away from home. Since it has been justified in terms of their being no alternative: it was what everybody did. 'Everybody' being the British community. It was part of a continuing endurance test, the legacy of the war. At the age of four to five all you understood was that you must have been very bad indeed for your parents, and in particular your mother, to send you away. The presence of your aunt was something of a consolation. When you behaved badly she was expected on several occasions to discipline you, which you knew to be unfair tactics. No one else had an aunt around who could be used in this way, (apart of course from your sister, who gave no trouble). Your mother's twin was a gentle soul though and used her own acceptable powers of persuasion.

The necessity laid on you to be dumb, not to tell anyone what had happened, is not a recovered memory, rather a later interpretation. However, in one of the hallucinatory episodes you knew that if you recovered then you deeply desired to be dumb. This was reflected in your visual memory of the three monkeys, a small brass version, very common in the Far East, which the family had owned. (See no evil, hear no evil, speak no evil.) Still in the hallucination you talked to your 'committee'; shared with them this necessity. They refused to allow it, telling you that part of your responsibility upon recovery would be to tell it how it was; to use your gift of fluency. The gesture of hand over mouth still holds emotive power for you.

So your mother spent the term-times with your father and younger brother and the whole family would be together only for the school holidays. You believe that you mother needed her twin sister with her, not so much because of the twin bond: they were close but not identical; had gone their own ways for years before this; but again in order to provide a protective screen between your father and yourself.

The memory of the abuse was confined to one place, possibly one incident (apart from being smacked which was accepted as normal). You have no doubt that this was a single aberrant event or short phase, in the tortured recovery process that your father was going through. He was not an habitual abuser. He was a healer; a physician; a man with a social conscience; charismatic; witty and talented in various ways. You were to come to admire him; to want to please him (which seemed impossible); to respect and to love but always to deeply fear him. If you tried to kiss him he would wipe it off, which you found hurtful.

Some of your hallucinatory experience included different representations of your father. They seemed to present a way forward, a way of coping. As 'Peter Rabbit' you knew that your father had been reduced to a mouse and was safely down his hole. Around you during these 'visions' were your committee. The committee consisted of your 'guardians', (an idea familiar to you from T.S Eliot's play 'The Cocktail Party'). Your local friends, people whom you know well, love and respect as well as your sister and brother-in-law were members; Pat your psychotherapist was present in these experiences from time to time. So there you were as Peter Rabbit, your father as a mouse, safely down his hole – but now the committee were trying to persuade you to let him out. 'He's tiny'; 'He won't do you any harm'; 'It's quite safe' and so on. In some trepidation you agree. When he emerges he turns out to be very witty, he makes you laugh – you know he is a 'platonic' mouse. This carries both the sense of a philosopher mouse and that of relationship without sex. Either way it is reassuring and Peter is more comfortable with the situation.

Another representation was of him as a cadet soldier, somehow involved, far too young, in the First World War: the war in which your grandfather, his father actually died. A line of war weary soldiers filters through the ward with your father amongst them. Your heart goes out to him – he is too young; desperately frightened; ragged; dirty and angry. It seems there is a choice and once again the decision is a shared one with the committee. It is agreed that we take him on board and make the future a brighter one for him. When you remember how he was then you still want to cry for him.

Yet again, the voice of your mother saying 'It's alright She, he's only a smelly old badger'. This was somehow linked with the physical revulsion you felt around him and yet were constrained by good manners not to express it, hardly even to yourself. When he got you to scratch his back you smiled and smiled and did so, but hated it and hated the greasy' spotty back with which you had to deal. Again his smell you associated with the wrap which you and your family gave him after the stroke. He wore it most of the time and long after his death, when you were ill, you asked to have it with you, somehow wanting a part of him, a safe part, near you.

In another hallucination he appeared, as he was after his stroke, dependent yet keeping his humour and his dignity, in many ways more approachable and not just because of physical necessity. You were there with him in the downstairs back room where he had his bed and where your

Where am I?   *Peter Rabbit*

Jeremy   *Sheila*   *The 'bear' theme*

parents spent most of the day. The knowledge was there that they knew what damage had been done to you as a child and they were amazed and grateful that despite that you helped in caring for him. You heard them describe you as a saint, you - the bad, the difficult, the unattractive child. There was great healing in that.

You and your sister pushed him through the stars in his wheel chair. It seemed entirely normal. She was Ursa Major - you Ursa Minor. Ursa Minor - the constellation that contains the pole star, the star to navigate by. Yet you were mad. You have no recollection of where the destination was supposed to be.

In the present you actually find these remembered images, the wisdom of your unconscious mind, very helpful. It appeared as if a way was given to you to cope with the recovered 'memory'. The memory of the event helped you to understand the long unhappiness of the years despite being surrounded since adulthood with fortunate circumstances and a loving home. The memory of the hallucinations gave pictures and words, which helped you in the process of self-integration.

Well that's enough about the possible roots of your psychosis. So it comes with love and respect from Sheila to Sheila.

4. BILL AND OTHER FAMILY ANXIETIES

September 22nd, 1998. Bill was my mother's only brother, seven years younger than she was. In kinship patterns the mother's brother always seems to hold a special place of affection and this was true of my relationship with him. He is much in my thoughts at present having died three weeks ago aged 77. This is not the place for his story but he was a General Practitioner in a village and both respected and loved. My sister and I went to live with him and his family during the school holidays. It had turned out that the preparatory school, to which we were being sent back in England, was in the same village. During the term time this made the school seem no less like a prison sentence. After Bill's funeral service we returned to his house that stands above the village and looks straight over the fields to this school. There it stood exactly as I remember it, cold, grey stone, unyielding yet set in lovely countryside. Neither the terms nor the holidays were easy. The school would have compared well with both Dickens' and Bronte's descriptions of earlier versions of such establishments.

On winter mornings we would find ourselves breaking the ice in our washbowls. There were not enough lavatories, which became particularly unpleasant when stomach bugs struck the children. Outdoor Nissen huts which acted as classrooms, were bitterly cold first thing in the morning, so writing was impossible. We all suffered from chilblains and chapped lips. The Head Mistress was a bully whom most of us loathed and feared. A combination of defiance, naughtiness and trouble with my work meant that much of my free time was spent either walking in single file, in silence around a circular path, standing in corners or trying to find this woman to see if my homework was yet up to scratch. It gave her satisfaction to reduce children to tears.

Once I wrote to my uncle and aunt begging to be taken away from school for at least the weekend. Either my letter was censored before it was even sent or the aunt contacted the school to find out what was happening. Either way I was in trouble and did not get the break that I hoped for. The sense of imprisonment deepened and despair went with it. On another occasion at the school in the Far East we'd been made to write a letter home after we'd been naughty. In it we had to tell our parents all the bad things that we had done. We awaited the consequences with a sense of impending doom. I only realised when I was much older that that letter would never have been sent. These kinds of experiences, where adults used both deception and manipulation against children, deepened my hatred and resentment of the system. It was not until my teens, however, that I began to question the inevitability of it all, to realise that there were other options, other possible choices. None of them seemed particularly attractive in the light of the apparent impossibility of actually living at home.

The holidays were made warmer by Bill's presence, but he was an overworked doctor, with a family and troubles of his own. I did not get on with his wife. Any maternal nature she possessed extended only as far as her own children - my younger cousins - and no further. I needed to be held, to belong, but instead felt alienated from this family. To take on the responsibility for two nieces who were four and six years older than your own eldest child, was a truly Christian response and one that would have been in accordance with the Book of their belief. It was possibly the best available solution at the time. The funeral revived memories of that period, together with sadness at the loss of Bill whom I loved.

Bound in with this loss has been another family anxiety. The brother who was born 13 years after myself, whom I watched growing up and whom I enjoyed whenever we were together, was diagnosed at the beginning of the year, as having multiple myeloma, a form of leukaemia. Shortly before the diagnosis had been made his partner became pregnant with their first child. The baby was born in June and is a lovely healthy being but is growing up with her parents facing all the stresses of the illness. The treatment is harrowing, involving radiotherapy, chemotherapy and the ever-present danger of overwhelming infection. The prognosis is of a greatly reduced life expectancy. All this is happening in London and as my sister lives there the burden of the caring is falling on her, while I try and support them all at a distance.

When I was first told of his diagnosis, I recalled the hallucinations that I had experienced, five years before, in which he featured. They were centred round his art, which is central to his work. I knew that it was under threat in some way and we sought to protect it by wrapping it in a capsule and burying it deep inside a stone wall. This was to protect it from radioactivity (which seemed to be an ever-present threat), but also from some kind of threat of plagiarism. He became in these hallucinations my 'blue eyed twin'. Even while I was fully aware that he wasn't in the literal sense. It happens that my eyes are brown and I suppose that there was some sense of balance. The imagery of these visions and the present events; with his life under threat from malignant cells; with his body being bombarded with radioactivity and with his siblings' blood being looked at for the possibility of marrow transplant, appeared to me as a kind of knowledge of the future. It was a juxtaposition which did not feel comfortable and which has made me rethink the nature of time and whether in certain states of consciousness linear time ceases to exist and the individual experiences the past, and future in the 'now'. The reading that I was undertaking at the time took this kind of knowledge for granted which was reassuring and which gave me a much-needed perspective. Examples of this reading would be Michael Talbot's book 'The Holographic Universe' (published by Harper Collins), and C.G.Jung's 'Synchronicity. An Acausal Connecting Principle', from his collected works 'The Structure and Dynamics of the Psyche'.

The blood tests for compatibility drew a blank. Not one of the remaining three of us is compatible with him. Given my blue-eyed twin 'vision' I fully expected to be donating my marrow and found an irony in the fact that I am actually compatible with my other younger brother, who also has blue eyes. Dreams and visions have to be interpreted symbolically. There is rarely a simple one-to-one relationship between the inner visual image and outer reality of one's life. There is often humour and pun involved as the unconscious mind communicates with our waking selves in this way.

There were other hallucinations around atomic power with an ever-present danger of it leaking through some of the encapsulations that were envisioned at the time. I experienced a transparent bubble constantly encircling me and remember Rachel sitting patiently by me, having to reach through the barrier to tidy my hair. At some point the vision was of being within a space capsule together with my mother's elder sister and perhaps one or two others whom I can't remember. The terror was of the rising level of cyanide within the space, together with the nauseating spinning motion.

The world, and we, were in terrible danger. Another example, this time free of poison, was the Chapter House of Wells Cathedral, sometimes within it and sometimes clinging to its exterior, in the company of others, as it seemed to spin through stars and space. There was always a strong international flavour to the company, with different languages being spoken and in particular Malay and Chinese with their associations with my childhood. In this world one just knew what the languages were as one does in a dream. As a child I only had a few words of either language.

Another vision was of First World War officers. My paternal grandfather was a regular soldier, a captain whose early career had been in India, where he had been involved with organising the Delhi Durbar (an Indian equivalent of the Edinburgh Tattoo). He had distinguished himself. With the outbreak of war he was in the front lines in France and the story was that he had been killed in a shooting accident. My father would have been two at the time. We learned later from a cousin that he had almost certainly committed suicide. Had this fact been made official his widow, my grandmother, would never have received the pension so necessary for her and her two children. My father had always been told and had believed the accident theory. The vision was also involved with radioactive or poison risk and I remember the uniform and the heavy boots of these family soldiers of mine, who were in some way trying to keep me safe. I adopted an army persona from time to time and remember, when I felt so weak, that even standing up required enormous self-discipline and I would talk to myself as if I was a soldier under command.

Looking at these images now I remember that I was being heavily drugged. In some way the unconscious was throwing up these warnings that quite apart from the internal threats from my own psyche there were very real external threats from this radical alteration of my body's normal physiology.

A summary of the drugs that I was on whilst hospitalised appears in the appendix.

5. THE GUARDIANS

Monday, January 25th, 1999

Another year has started and I feel encouraged with the progress my book is making. This is not so much due to my own writing that develops slowly but due to the interest people are showing and their willingness to write something for me.

Home life feels supportive and good. Work provides a constant, invigorating challenge, which only occasionally tips over into the stressful. On the whole I'm able to recognise the signs and take necessary measures to counteract this. Just at present I'm hoping to land a job, which would lead to a cut of hours in my present work and the equivalent hours in a related area. The two jobs together would mean that I would be able to teach Care Assistants, Registered Nurses and Student Nurses. The latter are beyond the scope of my present job. At 56 they may see me as too old - or ideal for a two-year contract.

In this chapter I want to write about my friends in the context of the experience of psychosis. I have represented them in the picture by the Guardian Tree in the bottom right hand corner. The tree is related to a twin pram (my mother's and aunt's) with Somerset cider apples close by; to myself as a student nurse, 'Ask the Patient' is written on the bed head; to the words 'The Shared Dream' which float in the space between the Tree and at my back to the nave and chancel of Wells Cathedral which rise above the tree. To the North West of the Tree as it were, but in another encapsulation, is a depiction of Fyne Court a building in the Quantock Hills.

I referred to my friends as 'The Guardians' using, or rather incorporating, an idea of T.S Eliot's, which he used in his verse play 'The Cocktail Party'. The idea of Guardian Angels has been associated with it in my mind. The dialogue in Act 1, Scene 2 goes like this:

Celia.   *What should we drink to?*
John.   *Whom shall we drink to?*
Celia.   *To the Guardians.*
John.   *To the Guardians?*
Celia.   *To the Guardians. It was you who spoke of guardians.*
          [They drink]

It may be that even Julia is a guardian.
Perhaps she is my guardian............

The Guardians, in the play, work behind the scenes to help their friends. They are self-effacing and act to bring about greater insight and fulfilment for these others. This strikes me now as somewhat patronising. The main Guardian is Sir Henry Harcourt-Reilly, a psychiatrist/psychoanalyst we are led to suppose.

My Guardians were close friends both at the time and since. They were not put off by the extremely bizarre behaviour that I was exhibiting. They were not put off by the mental hospital where I was an in-patient. They visited whenever they were allowed to and when they were able to. There were times when the staff determined that my list of visitors should be very restricted. The closed unit must have felt, for my friends, like entering and leaving a prison. It certainly felt like being in one to me.

The Guardian Angel association is illustrated in the heart of the drawing where angels surround the 'God-head'; the inspiration is taken from William Blake's pictures.   It encompasses the sense of some kind of protection throughout the ordeal, both from my earth(l)y friends and from another dimension. The names of these guardians are written on the branches and trunk of the Tree.

In the visions these friends together with my family constituted the Committee. I would seek their advice in the kind of National/World role that we were undertaking.

It is known that the 'mad' appear to be overwhelmed sometimes by grandiose ideas. They believe themselves to be God or Jesus Christ for example. They believe themselves to be capable of great feats of strength and daring. Clearly they are out of touch with everyday reality.   In my most grandiose moments I believed myself to be in 'sky control'. This control patently failed when the bomber jets screamed low over the hospital on their way to Bosnia. There was nothing hallucinatory about this fact. It was deeply disturbing and became part of the confusing world with which I had to deal.

But to go back to my Committee and to the visions - national rule had broken down (symbolic of the chaos in my psyche?) and the country was being ruled by small groups of skilled and good people, me together with my friends and family. It embarrasses my present self to confess this. So the town was under the guidance of the Committee. The skills represented were those of social work, teaching, medicine, nursing, artistic creativity (equated with God), computer use, mathematics, and psychotherapy.   We lived in our own family homes but our Centre was Fyne Court, an actual place on the Quantocks. It is a conservation area centred on the house, or what remains of a stately home.

Thinking about it now I remember that J and I were involved informally in the appointment of the first Warden. We had known David and Lynda in our Dorset days and knew that he would be a good man for the job. So we let both the appointing committee and David know of the other's existence. Lynda has always kept in touch with us and is one of my closest friends, counted among the Guardians.

I remember her visits both at hospital and at home. My hair, which was quite long at the time, began to irritate me and we went out into the courtyard on a sunny afternoon, where she cut it much shorter. I remember her concern as to whether this was what I really wanted. I also recall the near panic I felt and the self-control required just to sit still. On another occasion when she was looking after me in order to give J a break I put Mozart's piano concertos on and remember the sheer joy they gave me as I danced to them around the hall. Lynda joined in the spirit of the moment, dancing too - a brilliant, unshockable woman. She knew that when she came she would have to think of something active for us to do. I found it impossible to sit still, even while I was exhausted. I loathe housework and have had help in the house ever since I have returned to work and before, during the period in Sherborne when the children were tiny. However, despite this between us we did a complete 'summer' clean of the main bedroom, polishing and dusting and appreciating all the objects around as we did so. Throughout this period I knew that I had to 'endure'. It was a word that was frequently with me, sometimes expressed, but mostly just thought. The word has an adamantine quality and seems to give some of the strength that it possesses. I was also aware that I'd had some practice in my life during the long periods of misery separated from my parents.

This 'ruling group' knew that its members had the gift of eternal life and 'ordinary' mortals looked upon us with envy. There was even a fence separating the Quantocks from the surrounding area; we, the immortals, were the Lords of the Quantocks whilst the rest were beyond the pale. There was a knowledge that we were amongst the pagan gods of Greece and the Mediterranean: that we had access to all knowledge. We played among the hills.

Our work - and there was work - involved referring to the appropriate specialist within the Committee, but the strongest sense I have of this now is within the context of the Shared Dream. The Dream is written between my back and the Guardian Tree in the picture. It worked like this. In the night, if you were 'awake'; you asked around to see if anyone else in the group was also 'awake' if so and if they wanted to, you would dream travel together all over the world. In those travels trouble spots were visited and healed or helped in some way. These dreams were a source of great comfort and beauty to me. They seemed to come from a world that I had no conscious memory or idea of for much of their content.

The language is the language of the Dream. Over the years I have learned to take my more vivid dreams seriously and have sought to understand their message. I have used certain approaches, far from original to me. These include recording them. I became better at recalling them and working to 'fish' out the detail from the unconscious. The message was seen as one from my

Fyne Court.
Sheila as a student nurse.
'Ask the patient.'

The Guardian Tree

unconscious to my conscious self. In some way it would be righting a lost balance in my waking life. The people of the Dream, even while they are often recognisable as family, friends, acquaintances, historic figures or fictive figures were still not to be taken literally as that person. It was necessary to stand back and ask oneself what that person and more widely animals or objects represented in one's own psyche. I was fairly adept at this practice in the years leading up to 1993. Now I still use it if a dream shouts at me. It seems to me that the hallucination and the visions, which came to me during that period, can be approached in the same way.

How would I attempt an analysis of my Committee, the Quantocks, Fyne Court, immortality, the insiders and the outsiders? Any attempt that I make will be partial, but the other thing, which should be mentioned, is that dreams have to be interpreted in terms of the individual§ who dreamed the dream. While anyone reading this account might make a good stab at interpretation it has to feel a 'good fit' to the person who dreamed it. The dreamer must say 'amen' to it and must not be pushed to an alien understanding.

I would see the Committee as the acceptable side of myself, representing social concern, creativity, healing, love, teaching skills, together with pagan, earthy aspects (The Greek Gods), while those beyond the pale stand for the rejected self, the self which I do not wish to relate to, or own. The Shared Dream, the dream within the waking dream, reflects a deep social concern on a worldwide level. Perhaps I should involve myself more in action and less in unexpressed concern over these issues? Within the Shared Dream different aspects of the Self are talking to each other in the night and are feeling comfortable with this. Am I made up of many different facets of personality? Are we all? Indeed 'Who Am I'? This question is written in below the image of myself at the centre, bottom of the picture. It is not an easy one to answer.

The folk beyond the pale might be incorporated within the Jungian concept of the 'shadow' side of the personality. Jung saw one of the tasks of life as being the acknowledgement of the things about ourselves that we dislike and often repress into our unaware self. It may be equated with the things that we perceive as evil, bad or socially undesirable. The repression has probably happened very early in life in consequence of our upbringing. However, along with much that is probably not particularly helpful or good for us, we repress aspects of our being which help to lead to a rounded, wholesome and creative personality. We need to get in touch with the whole of whom we are in order to determine consciously which bits we will allow and which bits disallow. Taken to extremes when this process remains largely unconscious it might lead to some kind of splitting of the personality. The images in the Quantock vision seem to be showing the acceptable and the unacceptable sides of my psyche. They are there in my memory to be looked at and worked with. Why madness? We are all somewhere on a spectrum that runs from absolute sanity to absolute insanity. Is there anyone on either extreme? I suspect that most of us fall somewhere in the middle of the spectrum and in my own case I spent some months very close to the extreme end of insanity. Every society will have its own definition of sanity and acceptable behaviour. Furthermore, in complex societies there will be many subgroups that will vary markedly from one another in this respect.

The loss of touch with 'reality' is the characteristic that separates psychosis from neurosis or depression. The individual has no control over it some of the time. Why are some people affected and not others? It may be to do with their basic nature, but almost certainly there will be environmental factors and the person who has repressed too much of themselves into the unconscious self may come to pay the price. This repression takes place in the face of intolerable pain. It is possible that it takes some kind of mental energy to repress memory and aspects of who we are. In my case I believe I ran out of spare energy and out of the ability to control the unconscious content of my mind. There are many thinkers who simply do not accept the reality of the unconscious mind, but I have found it the most useful way to interpret my psyche.

It's now a few days later and thinking of Jung and the unconscious mind has sent me back to reread 'Memories, Dreams, Reflections' (which was co-written in his old age by Jung and Aniela Jaffe, (The Fontana Library)); together with 'Jung, Selected Writings', introduced by Anthony Storr (Fontana Paperback). Jung would be my authority on this psychodynamic way of thinking and I first read some of his work many years ago. Reading it again I am struck by the loneliness of his position at the time when he wrote. Although profoundly influenced by Freud he was to develop a different understanding of the way the mind works and allowed for the spiritual, or the soul, in a way that Freud did not. Both were scientists, both doctors but perhaps where Freud strove to contain his theories within the parameters of the scientific 'experiment', Jung moved into an area of thought which was both. For instance, in Memories – in the prologue - he writes:

'Science works with concepts of averages which are far too general to do justice to the subjective variety of an individual life' (p.17, 1967 Edition)
and again on the same page

'I can only make direct statements, only "tell stories". Whether or not the stories are "true" is not the problem. The only question is whether what I tell is my fable, my truth.'

This would express for me my own stance when I tell of my childhood experiences.

Jung had well-differentiated figures in his fantasy world. Philemon was one example. Jung says of him in 'Memories':

'Psychologically, Philemon represented superior insight. He was a mysterious figure to me. At times he seemed to me quite real, as if he were a living personality. I went walking up and down the garden with him, and to

me he was what the Indians call a guru.' (p. 208)

Another example was his Anima figure, the female principle in his psyche. He used her in dialogue and in writing and recognised both negative and positive aspects in her. He equates her with a primitive soul. Women have an equivalent male figure, the animus. These soul figures can be destructive and need to be wrestled with and brought into conscious awareness. Jung says in the same edition

'In the final analysis the decisive factor is always consciousness, which can understand the manifestations of the unconscious and take up a position towards them.' (p. 212)

He was a true frontiersman of the psyche and it is a comfort to me that he is, in a very real way, another of my Guardians: that he has travelled first and further.

I am also struck by the sheer length of time that might elapse between the experience of a vision or fantasy and the complete understanding of it. He shared some of his earlier dream material with very few people and then only long after. He was 65 before he shared what he calls his phallus dream with anyone. At the time of the dream he was three or four. I have become increasingly aware that the understanding of one's dreams, visions and imaginings takes place slowly: that the unconscious mind is not ruled by linear time and cannot be rushed. After my final discharge from hospital the only material I felt able to work with was that of the hallucinatory images by way of drawing. I was not ready to write or to attempt any detailed analysis. The drawing seemed the best way to capture the 'inner' sight. It was only three and a half years later when the picture was finished that I began to think about writing. The process of drawing drew me back to the inner experience and back to the damaged child precisely because I was doing something in drawing and colouring that she would have done.

Thinking more widely about my Guardians I realise that as well as Jung; the poetry of Gerard Manley Hopkins; the novels of George Elliot; the poems and plays of T.S Eliot and William Blake's writing and illustrations were all there during my illness as a kind of background and support. The detail was not there merely the knowledge of their importance to me, so that as I recovered I knew that they were part of the furniture of my mind and could always be turned to both internally and externally in order to deepen my knowledge of them.

At one stage after I had been readmitted to hospital, I became profoundly depressed, agitated and had a persistent (as they are) delusion that I was going to die. At this point, while I was on a weekend 'leave' at home, John and Andy dropped in. Life was becoming unbearable that day and I couldn't bear the thought of returning to the ward early. So they took me home; gave me lunch; walked me around their garden; introduced me to their donkey and simply hugged me – what guardianship. It seems wrong to single any of my friends out: they were all so good to me.

6. SHAKESPEARE, MADNESS AND MYSELF

Monday, February 22nd, 1999
I have been to see 'Shakespeare in Love' twice over the last few weeks and was
hugely entertained by it. Every summer since '77, except for '93 when I was ill
and Jeremy went alone, we have spent two weeks camping at Stratford with a
group of teachers and pupils from the school which J taught at in Hertfordshire.
For the first year he was still the Deputy Head there and by the summer of 1978
we had already moved to Somerset and his new job. However, we continued to
take part in the Stratford fortnight. The purpose of these camps was, and is,
Shakespeare's plays. In '77, at the age of 35, I had studied his plays at school for
'O' level and 'A' level, but had had little more exposure apart from seeing an
occasional performance. Then I went along out of duty and we went as a family.
The first year Rachel would have been eight, Jo seven and Ben five. They came
with us to some of the plays; otherwise one of the adults would stay back on the
campsite and baby-sit for both our children and those of other teachers. Over
the years as I have read the plays, heard them lectured on, discussed and most
importantly seen them done in a variety of different ways, I have grown to love
them and Shakespeare's language.

One of the clearer memories that I have of the week before my admission
was the terrifying knowledge that I seemed to be losing control – going mad.
One of the reasons for my fear was a lack of trust in what I knew of mental
hospitals in general and our local one in particular. Large, impersonal, full of
empty corridors leading to unknown areas where one could easily get lost, dirty,
ugly furniture in a poor state of repair, no privacy and full of people who's
behaviour might be unpredictable. (I'm not only thinking of patients). The
description is as true of the hospital where I spent three months of my training,
as a student nurse in the 60s, as it is of the local one to which I was admitted as
a patient in the 90s. Both institutions are now 'closed' with many of the
personnel continuing to work in the 'community'.

I remember asking to be treated like the Gaoler's Daughter in 'The Two
Noble Kinsman'. Only J understood the reference to one of Shakespeare's least
known plays, thought to have been written with Fletcher. We saw it in the
summer of 1986 with Imogen Stubbs as the Gaoler's Daughter and it made a
deep impression on me. She is never given a name; perhaps the intention in the

subplot was to focus on a situation and social 'types' rather than individuals.
First there is the recognition of a problem, then the need to ascribe a cause.

Wooer.   *'Was she well? Was she in health sir?*
              When did she sleep?'............

Gaoler.   *I do not think she was very well, for now*
              You make me mind her, but this very day
              I asked her questions, and she answered me
              So far from what she was, so childishly,
              So sillily, as if she were a fool,
              An innocent, and I was very angry.'.................

Wooer.   *'Tis too true, she is mad.'*............

Gaoler.   *'I half suspected*
              What you have told me; the gods comfort her!
              Either this was her love to Palamon,
              Or fear of my miscarrying on his 'scape'
              Or both.'

In this passage we find emphasised the importance of sleep; the recognition
by the Gaoler that she was *'so far from what she was'*; then his
acknowledgement that he hadn't quite been able to face the evidence before
him, *'I half suspected'*; together with his immediate concern for the possible
causes. The wooer goes on to describe how he found her and we have the
themes of singing, nonsense, flowers, willows, emotional lability and a focus on
the subject of immediate concern, which recur repeatedly when Shakespeare
describes madness. The Wooer follows her to ensure her safety before returning
to inform the father of her distress. A company then returns with her and
through the dialogue runs the note of loss of normal inhibition (this also occurs
with Ophelia). Her brother advises the Gaoler

'By no means cross her; she is then distempered
Far worse than now she shows.

The way this passage of the play was produced in the performance was with
rustic dancing, singing and the gentle restraint of the daughter. There was a
harness, if I remember correctly, but she was not isolated. She was taken up
within the company, was part of it and there was a great sense of compassion
and wisdom prevailing.

The doctor watches his patient, remarks that her moods probably swing
with the moon and he listens to the Gaoler's description of her:

'She is continuously in a harmless distemper, sleeps little, altogether
without appetite save often drinking; dreaming of another world, and a
better;.......'

Then the doctor advises the wooer to pretend to be Palamon (the nobleman
who was imprisoned in her father's gaol and with whom she fell hopelessly in

love). The deceit is seen as of little concern if this device will help her back to sanity. His advice to the wooer is to satisfy her with sexual intercourse, if that is what she wants, as this will be part of the remedy. The father is not quite sure about this one, but his main desire is for her recovery. We are left feeling hopeful that all will be well and that the subterfuge will dissolve as her sense of reality returns. Perhaps the only part of the advice that I am less than happy with is this dissimulation. The carers need to be very secure in their own grasp of reality and to run the risk of increasing the sufferer's sense of confusion is not a kindness.

So what did I hope for when I asked to be treated in this way? Perhaps I hoped for containment within the family; a wise physician; and the willingness to listen to, to look for, the inner meaning of the external manifestation. At the time I could only ask to be treated like the Gaoler's Daughter.

However often I have seen one of the plays there is always something new, some insight which I haven't been ready for before or which the director has emphasised in this particular production. The portrayal of madness in different sets of circumstances with varying outcomes held a fascination for me long before the illness. As if a part of my psyche knew that this would affect me very closely.

What happens to King Lear and his judgement in his older age? The Earl of Kent, a faithful servant to him, risks his wrath:

'............. *be Kent unmannerly,*
When Lear is mad. What would'st thou do, old man?
Think'st thou that duty shall have dread to speak
When power to flattery bows?'

Kent is criticising King Lear, which took courage, for abdicating his power to his three daughters. He knows that the flattering speeches of Lear's two elder daughters are meaningless and that trouble will surely follow.

Lear was in great need of true friends but in his hubris he was not prepared to listen to advice. He had failed to share his plans until he revealed them in public, as if part of him had known that his wiser counsellors would have tried to restrain him. Once his plans were publicly revealed he could brook no resistance and this in the very act of laying down his power. He actually threatens Kent's life, whose response is to say:

'*Kill thy physician, and the fee bestow*
Upon the foul disease. Revoke thy gift;
Or, whilst I can vent clamour from my throat,
I'll tell thee thou dost evil'.

Kent is banished for his pains. Rather than going he assumes a disguise and continues to act in the role of protector to the King.

The plot moves on with Goneril and Regan, the two daughters who have professed their love of their father in exaggerated terms, in order to get their

| Home | Mount Olympus | Sheila aged four |

| Peter | Jeremy | Sheila |

Shakespeare's 'mad' characters named

share of his kingdom, now driving the King completely out of the sphere of his control. They refuse him his dignity; they refuse him his normal retinue; his comforts; and drive him between their two kingdoms, which ironically they have received as a gift at his hands. They divide and rule and between them turn their father's mind from infirmity and poor judgement to madness. In his madness he finds a compassion for others which one suspects has not been a part of his character before.

At the end of the play Lear's third daughter Cordelia reappears. She refused to exaggerate her love for her father and in consequence sacrifices the third of his kingdom that should have been hers. For the passage of the play, she has been banished to France, then returning with the French army she is hoping to restore some kind of balance and justice, having heard what has happened to her father. Seeking a doctor to help him, she hopes that something may be done. The doctor tells her

'There is means, Madam;
Our foster-nurse of nature is repose,
The which he lacks; that to provoke in him,
Are many simples operative, whose power
Will close the eye of anguish.'

And Cordelia's response:

'All bless'd secrets,
All you unpublish'd virtues of the earth,
Spring with my tears! Be aidant and remediate
In the good man's distress! Seek, seek for him,
Lest his ungovern'd rage dissolve the life
That wants the means to lead it:'

These quotations, referring to the Elizabethan knowledge of herbs as a basis of drugs, show both Cordelia's and the physician's awareness of the importance of sleep. They also show that Cordelia's perception of her father is of a 'good' man, overtaken by rage which could cause his death. In modern terms, he desperately needs sleep. His body is using a level of adrenaline, which apart from allowing him no rest has driven him from sources of food and the desire to eat it, so that his life is at risk. Finally, there is no escape for Lear. He gets rest and is reunited with Cordelia. She is captured and killed by her sisters' forces and the King dies in overwhelming grief.

Shakespeare conveys the experience of madness/psychosis from many angles. He shows the anguish and tragedy of the person suffering it (as in Lear, Ophelia, Lady Macbeth and the Gaoler's daughter). He shows the 'put on' madness of Edgar in King Lear and of Hamlet, although in the latter case people will disagree as to whether Hamlet was truly mad at any point or not. He also shows Malvolio, in 'Twelfth Night' almost being driven mad, by the cruel practical joke played of treating him as mad and locking him away.

His observations of madness are acute and the classic symptoms are described. His portrayal of the 'good' physician is equally powerful. The doctor portrayed in 'Macbeth' is scrupulous in seeking facts, in recording what he hears, in recognising that a disease may be *'beyond my practice'*.

He goes on:

'Unnatural deeds
Do breed unnatural troubles: infected minds
To their deaf pillows will discharge their secrets.
More needs she the divine than the physician. -
God, God forgive us all! Look after her;
Remove from her the means of all annoyance,
And still keep eyes upon her.'

In his later talk with Macbeth the doctor is troubled by the sense that an evil act has provoked Lady Macbeth's unbalanced mind,

'Not so sick, my Lord,
As she is troubled with thick-coming fancies,
That keep her from her rest'.

And Macbeth begs him:

'Canst thou not minister to a mind diseased,
Pluck from the memory a rooted sorrow,
Raze out the written troubles of the brain,
And with some sweet oblivious antidote
Cleanse the stuff'd bosom of that perilous stuff
Which weighs upon the heart?'

To which the doctor replies:

'Therein the patient
Must minister to himself.'

The doctor is aware that it is not just his 'patient' who needs forgiveness but the society in which they lived. He is treading carefully, no doubt very aware that Macbeth is guilty in some way.

I wonder whether we do any better for those in mental distress in modern times than is described by Shakespeare and presumably acted upon then, in real life as well as in drama? Some so-called treatments can be barbaric at the worst and temporarily helpful at best (e.g. Electro-Convulsive Therapy and those anti-psychotic drugs which can lead to long-term physical and mental dysfunction). Within psychiatry, some wisdom has been lost and little gained in terms of specialist knowledge except an attempt at diagnostic certainty, which does not stand up to scrutiny. Our health service is prepared to pay expensive consultant fees but not to offer psychotherapy to those who might benefit more from that than from the other more conventional psychiatric approaches. Of course, some psychiatrists use psychotherapy/analysis as part of their treatment approach and this is to be welcomed.

In the last analysis I believe our own society is no less sick, albeit in different ways, than the one described in 'Macbeth' – so one might say with the physician, 'God, God forgive us all!'

7. ENDURING A TERRIBLE TIME – JEREMY'S PERSPECTIVE

This bit of the story begins on the night of 25th-26th May1993, but the roots go back and there had been telltale signs that Sheila was not well. Running a hospital ward is never easy and always takes it out of one. Normally Sheila could, to a certain extent, shrug the pressure off while at home and unwind a bit. But this time she did not. What followed seemed to unfold as a terrible time for us all, a tragedy. Now, with hindsight and the awareness of what has happened since, it looks different: almost like a triumph (which we were experiencing as a disaster); something we can remain calm about as we re-look it all in the eye; suffering which -paradoxically -has led to blessing, for us and others.

My version of what happened starts by tracing some of the recent roots that led to Sheila's illness. The story then records her week in bed at home before her admission into hospital. There followed the relief of her being discharged in July. After about a month she had to return to hospital and we had to come to terms with that. At that stage I took a short break. Autumn came and things gradually improved. Sheila started coming home again, first for short spells and then for good; and we have subsequently watched and admired her return to work and sought to make sense of what we had been through.

There will be overlap with what others have written. There will be some omissions, even some contradictions or contrasting views. What I went through so intensely, daily, has somehow slipped away in the four years that have passed and I am conscious that much detail and perplexity, times of amazement and real difficulty, are glided over and are no longer recallable.

Here then is an eye-witness's account of what took place between the end of May and the end of October, 1993 but not set down until mid-1997.

Telltale Signs

That May Sheila was unusually tired and strained. We had visited a Henry Moore Exhibition at the Chesil Gallery at which I had tasted oysters for the first time and Sheila had shown no real interest in the sculptures or the people. She complained of being tired. She remained detached and strangely silent. 'Take me home,' was what her gestures and body seemed to be saying.

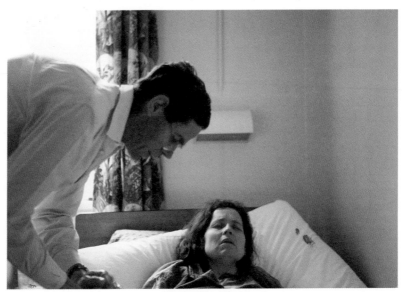

Jeremy as carer

Not long after she had drawn and painted herself in a portrait - for Ben's coming twenty-first birthday - setting up her painting things in the dining room. She added a portrait of me so that it became a double portrait. She worked with great concentration, expressing some alarm at the picture of her that was emerging. Was she frightened by the face she found looking back at her? Did she sense that it was unusually sad? She had resolved she had to depict herself truthfully; and she did that. I sketched her painting her self-portrait (see illustrations).

The watercolour done (see Ben's chapter) it was clear that the effort had both tired and exhilarated her. The result was a considerable achievement, a first, a big step forward for her, something she had thought of doing for some time. And the picture was handed over to Ben in his room in Birmingham on his birthday, a Sunday. The journey there and back in a day was inevitably rather tiring but we were pleased that we had celebrated with Ben. Another contributory cause to the tiredness and strain was the research that Sheila was doing. This was for an M. Phil at Exeter. A member of their Psychology Department was supervising her. She was researching the effects of panic attacks on sufferers from chronic chest conditions and investigating the possibility of their being given some psychological means of getting relief. This work involved tutorials and some training at Exeter, a regular study day away from the ward as well as case studies of selected patients, known to the consultant and her ward, who had agreed to take part.

She was interested in discovering ways in which she could help the chronically breathless to relax when their difficulty in breathing was made worse by fear. One of the techniques she was trying out was the use of relaxation tapes which encouraged one to let go, breathe calmly and relax as much as possible. A clinical psychologist had given her a stock of these tapes, which she was enthusiastically recommending to her clients along with breathing exercises and other practical steps.

Her full-time, five days a week job, which could include week-ends (but rarely nights), was normally spent running the acute chest ward. But while she was doing her research and during Exeter University's term time she was given one day a week (out of her five) to concentrate on her research. That meant that she might spend several hours driving to see people in their homes in Chard or Bridgwater, for instance. While with them she would talk to them, note their progress, and ask a target group to try certain things.

This was interesting research, thoroughly worthwhile, well intentioned, and needed, too, but it added to the strain and pressure on her. For not only was she trying to help a sick person who had his or her own anxieties and acute condition but the husband or wife would also be anxious and need reassurance and advice and time to chat with Sheila. At home we did question her workload, especially since the research inevitably was getting done in her evenings and spare time. But we concluded that she could manage both knowing she would plan carefully and that she had support.

Ironically the researcher was suddenly to find herself having panic attacks (though not because of breathing problems) and she needed to play the relaxation tape.

'I can't make it to work today': the First Day

We have reached the last week in May, at the end of which we were due to fly to France (during the school's half-term) for a week's walking. But during the night of Tuesday 25th May she was restless, wide-awake and talkative.

I now draw on brief notes, which I began the following morning. At times, over the next few days, I also attempted sketches of her, generally done very hurriedly, in an attempt to depict what she was going through. These drawings, however primitive, helped me both to practise my sketching and to come to terms with what I was experiencing. They enabled a partial distancing and detachment to take place.

Imagine, then, Sheila restless in the early hours, complaining and spilling out her thoughts. We talk; have a kind of conversation, which ran on these lines:

'I'm tired! I can't eat. I'm absolutely knackered...Am I going mad?' (That's a frightening enough question for the listener as well as for the speaker.) 'I am getting like P who had had some mental illness....I've been trusting my body...I believe if I can talk and write, I'm safe. But that's not so any more. Words are so important.'

I tried to comfort her and said she had been a 'good enough' mother.

She began to doubt whether her mother had been a good enough mother. She complained of her mouth being dry and of having acute indigestion. She had earlier taken two paracetamols.

She continued talking and reflected that she had been busy being her own little psychotherapist, and invited me to ask her mother's twin sister and her husband what she was like aged five. This thought had been triggered by an event on the ward a few days before. A five-year-old girl had visited her. The girl's father had died (on the ward) in his sixties from a stroke the previous week. He had a very mature and loving wife who was looking after their two children aged seven and five. Suddenly, without any warning, the five year old was in her office, wanting comfort. 'What was I supposed to do when I was not coping with anything?' Sheila asked. The day had dragged on and on. She had shared this experience with the ward (staff) and they had said, 'Sister, go home!'

Earlier on a previous day she had brought some mugs in from home (for the staff's use) and then she had seen these mugs on the ward. 'What are these doing here?' she had thought. (She normally liked to keep home and work separate: it was her way of coping.) 'It's day mares', she had decided.

She had slept well up to the last weekend, she reflected and generally had felt fine. Art was good. She had felt in control. The self-portrait? 'It's grand and

Jeremy's sketch of me attempting a self-portrait

great' but she 'couldn't hack little girls. They're so honest and beautiful'.

She started blaming her parents who, she felt, hadn't valued her at all. As a result she had spent her life trying to build up her self-esteem. She felt she had to go on making amends for her mother. Her mother had been all right for she had found Sheila's father. But she (Sheila) had been spread among the family. She had been a difficult child. 'That's the simple unwinding of it.'

There was more talk that night in a similar vein. She pointed out that labelling diminishes one. She felt she needed help but was sceptical about GPs: 'they fuck me up'. (This has been a refrain of hers in sickness and in health!)

When morning came, Sheila announced, 'I can't make it to work!' I decided to go to work (to my teaching) though I was worried about Sheila. Fortunately Rachel, our eldest, was at home and could look after her.

At school my senior colleagues persuaded me to go home and said I was to put Sheila first. Back at home I found that Rachel was coping well. As she did something for her mother she would get comments and tips about nursing. Sheila was clearly ill yet she could not stop teaching, at one point commenting dryly, 'you'll not make much of a nurse if you do it that way!' We, her parents, were very fortunate that Rachel was at home for much of this coming spell. Her help, companionship, calmness and common sense were invaluable: I could not have managed my job and supporting Sheila without first her and then Jo.

That Wednesday morning passed with Sheila fearful, angry, tearful and generally edgy. She wanted to speak to Pat, a psychotherapist whom she would visit occasionally and had left a message for Pat to phone her. She got up and paced around, waiting for that phone call.

Finally at 12.30 it came. She described to Pat how she had felt aged three and a half when her father had come home for the first time (having been a prisoner of war of the Japanese); and how later, after her brother's birth, she had smashed a doll in her rage. Her sister, who was two years older, carried the love and beauty. Yet she (Sheila) had strong fantasy links with her father. He was a doctor and he had a lot of power. She felt cross, too, about being packed off to boarding school. 'Why put a child into boarding school aged five?' She ironically carried the guilt of being a naughty child. But he had been damaged by his long internment, which had humiliated him. (She was longing for some reassurance, which I gave her. Thinking of her first memories of her father was upsetting her.) She told Pat, 'He never let me kiss him. He wiped off my kisses. He was lazy, self-indulgent, sexist'. She went on to complain that 'Mum colluded to keep the family together'; and she concluded, 'so I have therefore survived all that'.

There was more she wanted to tell Pat about her father: 'he didn't face me, confront me, relate to me at all'. But maybe 'he had come back from internment changed?' Her mother had had to make choices. Sheila observed wryly that she herself was married to a doctor (of education) and was becoming one herself, should her research eventually lead on to a doctorate!

That afternoon, back in school, in Assembly I told the story of how John Hillaby and his wife had spun a coin in order to decide when to leave Venice by train for Greece; and the answer had been to take the later one, twenty-four hours on; and how when they were on it they came across a terrible train crash. The train they would have been on, had they left at the earlier time, was the one that was smashed up. I linked this to making one's choices by going 'with the flow' of our feelings and the circumstances at the time.

Afterwards a member of staff came up to thank me and said that the story had helped her to make a decision that she had been putting off. Within forty-eight hours I had to cancel our proposed flight to Marseilles and week's holiday that would have begun that Sunday.

My recollection is that we had visits at home that afternoon/evening both from Pat who came to be with Sheila and from our GP whose arrival prompted Sheila to remark, 'don't let them get their mitts on it'. Our doctor asked, 'has this (illness) happened before?'. 'No', I said. He described it as a one-off acute crisis, but he admitted that he did not know much about mental illness. He gave me a prescription, his main concern being to help Sheila to sleep. About six that evening Sheila asked, 'I'm going to survive this, aren't I?' 'You are,' I said.

The Second Day

We had spent the first day adjusting to the fact that Sheila was not well enough to work, was not sleeping much, had much to say which was both sense and some things which appeared near 'non-sense' to us but clearly made sense to her. We were not sure what was going on. Was this the start of an illness? Was she just overtired? If so, then rest and time at home would sort that out. I was still hoping that she would be well enough to go on holiday that coming weekend. There were still two days before half-term.

The second day, Thursday, 27th May was spent in organising ourselves at home so that we had a suitable routine and could best look after Sheila's needs which she described succinctly as those of 'a three and a half year old'.

I left for work, leaving Rachel looking after Sheila, who stayed in bed all day, coming home at about 3.0 pm. Sheila made two phone calls after I had returned. The first was to her aunt (elder sister to her mother). This aunt sought to reassure her about some of her fears and worries, suggested her daughter, (Sheila's first cousin) as a good person to talk to and promised to try and see Sheila one day soon. Sheila, it appeared, was on a quest, in pursuit of her early years.

The second conversation was with Pat again. It was a jumble of sharing what she was going through while underneath there was an unspoken question. She could not be sure how much sleep she had had; she was teaching Rachel how to nurse; she realised something new and alarming was happening to her: 'I think it's going to take a hell of a long time!' However she still had her sense of humour, along with a sense of urgency, even desperation. Next she spoke of madness in Shakespeare. For instance of the Gaoler's Daughter in Shakespeare/Fletcher's 'Two Noble Kinsmen'; and I realised, as would have Pat, that she was worried that she was going mad. This was the unspoken question. It was a terrifying prospect - for her and for us.

I don't remember discussing it with Rachel at this stage. Perhaps because it was the worst of all our fears, being something almost unbearably painful to name. That day, and regularly after, Rachel and I compared notes in order to keep each other up-to-date.

To return to that long snake of a phone conversation which wriggled from one topic to the next with Sheila doing most of the talking. She admitted to Pat that she was concerned about what had happened to her in the past and could not talk to her cousin, since she was in New York. At one point she described herself as manic; and later she reckoned she had 'not really slept yet'. To end she asked Pat to feedback both what she had learnt from that phone call and what she thought might be happening to her. I gathered that Pat did not know, like the rest of us, exactly what was unfolding and was as open and supportive as she could be.

It was a difficult situation for Pat. I would have liked the chance to ask her whether I should discourage Sheila from asking too many questions but it was Sheila's phone call. I concluded that I had to rely on common sense in working out what to do and say.

A feature or characteristic of the whole experience was this: we were constantly aware that we were travelling into new territory. We had not been through anything like this before. There was no one to tell us what was going to happen. The doctor, Pat, no one could be sure. This was a 'first' for them and for us. There seemed to be a parable at the heart of it all, which we had to 'unlock', read and go along with. Only the parable was not someone else's story that we were reading or listening to. It was ours. We were the actors. We were living it as well as having to make sense of it. We had to respond to each moment, each development, as it happened, in the best way we could with what we had got. We were alone.

Yet we were not alone, paradoxically. In a way that I cannot explain, with my 1997 hindsight and knowledge, I see that we were never alone - even though we felt we were. Someone was with us, even if that someone was not physically present to be consulted. My interpretation of this, drawing on my Christian view of things, is that in our darkness and stumbling, in our agonies and pain, Christ was with us even though we were not aware of it, and that He was helping us to bring good out of the horror of seeing Sheila suffer so. That is a personal view. Others close to all this would argue differently or feel dissatisfied with such an explanation.

To support my view I would add that throughout I relied on prayer, I continued to meditate, finding that I had to seek help for us in this way, believing that it worked but not necessarily getting any clear evidence that it was making

And a bib after.

Suffering
later 2-6-93
(done at speed)

More rapid sketches by Jeremy -
In the top one I look like a child

a difference at the time. Praying was what I could do - and wanted to do. It was a crucial way in which I could contribute.

That digression was necessary if only to answer the question 'what kept you going while Sheila was ill?' The full answer is my family, friends, and close colleagues at work, they helped enormously and I had to use my faith.

After Sheila's chat with Pat, I realised, as I think Pat knew and Rachel was also aware, that Sheila felt that a kind of madness was overtaking her. Sheila told me afterwards that she thought Pat had accepted her view of things, her truth.

We settled down for what was to be another disturbed night. And so ended our second, topsy-turvy day.

The Third Day

Things took a turn for the worse. Alternatively one could say it became clearer that Sheila was very ill and we had to face that. By the time I left for school I knew that I had to cancel our coming walking holiday. But first there had been the night to get through.

We both got little sleep. Sheila slept for an hour after taking two sleeping tablets. Then she was awake more or less from midnight onwards. At 12.30 she had a drink of lactate and milk and took three tablets (she had been prescribed two sorts, at least) and three-quarters of an hour later she went down to the kitchen and did some writing. She returned soon after 2.00, took two more sleeping pills and then some three hours later became very upset. She cried, she sobbed. She sat up. Her moans got louder. She rocked herself, then sat on the side of the bed, wailing. She rocked and bounced and lay back. I felt that she was lost to me. Would she ever return to normality? It was a very dark time.

Again she lay back, her head on my knee, close to screaming. She sat up before shifting to lie on her back across me, and she called out, 'O, Christ!' I held her and comforted her. But she was not aware of me. Slowly she settled and stilled. I talked to her.

She was worried that she would become manic. She started giving orders, keeping control of the situation as far as she could. She wanted to see the doctor; for Pat to be kept informed; and for me to keep a medication chart and to go on taking notes.

I noted that the time was about 6.15 and made her a milk drink. Her throat was very dry.

The doctor's appointment was arranged for about midday but we had to cross town and go to the other surgery. Rachel drove while I sat with Sheila in the back. She was frightened and panicky as we travelled. She feared she was going to die -'for the family', as a scapegoat. We had difficulty in getting her into the surgery, so weak was she on her feet and so withdrawn.

The same happened when we took her along the corridor for the appointment. Was she play-acting a bit to impress the doctor? He seemed baffled, said he could not do much or be sure what was happening. He prescribed an inhaler to help her, should she start coughing in the night. He may also have said that he would contact the consultant psychiatrist.

That afternoon we got her to the settee in the hall where she listened to the relaxation tape and tried saying 'Om', as it recommended, to calm herself.

The next development was that Dr. Ahmed, the consultant psychiatrist, called. He talked to Sheila for some forty minutes and then to me. I told him what had happened and what I had noticed. He wanted us to quieten her down so that she could rest and build up her strength. She could then do some 'focused' work with Pat. He could not be sure whether this episode was the onset of a mental illness or not. There was evidence of disassociation and yet she was very rational for much of the time.

Meanwhile our GP had phoned and had prescribed Stelazine (one tablet at night) and Temazepam (the same - with even a second, one hour later). These were intended to dampen Sheila down. We were warned that she might have a dry mouth and some blurred vision. He would keep in touch.

Into the Fourth Day

That night once more neither of us had much sleep. We dozed or drowsed. We put the relaxation tape on quietly, and we played it over and over until I could gladly have chucked a book at it! I tried to say quietly to myself the phrase 'My Peace I give unto you' in order to stay calm and to help Sheila.

By this stage half-term had started. It was already becoming clear that it was right to cancel the walking holiday, disappointed as I had felt about that. The priority was to look after Sheila, to get her well again. At least I had a week to concentrate on that.

That Saturday morning we breakfasted early with Sheila having a second milk drink and being concerned about her pulse. During the night she had had two bouts of screaming. A terrible sound, which I hoped Rachel could not hear. This had been brought on by her dreaming that she was being crucified.

My notes say nothing about Saturday, 29th May until around midday when Pat and her husband came to see us. Pat had a long talk with Sheila while I chatted to him. It was very kind of them to drive over. Pat wanted us to keep Sheila eating and hoped that she would not try to put the world to rights. She was a bit worried by Sheila's religious language but was happier with the symbolism behind it. On our side we were all hoping, I suspect, that the cure or answer would come from Pat, aided by the GP's tablets, rather than from the more ominous-sounding psychiatric side represented by Dr. Ahmed. .

Later that day I was cycling back from the canal when I suddenly had the fear or fantasy that Sheila might show her face at the window or do something suicidal. There was no sign of that, fortunately. But when I took her a drink of Complan, she told me she had been shouting out to the neighbours that she had got healing hands, her father's hands.

At this point she began to make claims, which were out of character (about the great things she could do) and which did suggest that she was not well. Her voice went husky, too. She wanted to save Bosnia. In her world there would be no bombing and no killing. There would be peace within families and between nations. It would be a beautiful, loving and tender world. Much of what she was saying was very lucid and worthwhile. She poured out these wishes for our world to the background sounds of the relaxation tape, which was much more bearable by day than at night!

I spent much of my time upstairs with her and I tried a bit of sketching and light painting. Shakespeare's play 'Macbeth' came up in conversation. We were thinking about Lady Macbeth's illness, which deteriorated into madness and how Macbeth looked to the doctor to cure her. He couldn't. That thought left us both sad and anxious.

Sunday, the Fifth Day

Sheila felt very tired that morning. Rachel looked after her while I went to church. Sheila rang Pat when I was out. The GP called (did we ask him to?) and reported that her pulse rate was 90 and that her chest was clear. She could finish the temazepam and I could have one that night. He would see Sheila if she needed to go to the surgery.

I found I needed to have little breaks from the wear and stress of the illness and so I went to see friends (a couple, she was Senior Teacher at the school) to have a chat and to let them know what was happening. With them I could relax and joke and get rid of some of the tension.

On my return Rachel greeted me with the news that Sheila had taken herself out into the garden. She was agitated and in a loud voice had addressed the neighbours and the world. She had then come in, her mission accomplished and lain down on the hall sofa where she had been very restless. She had bruised her wrist below the palm by swinging it against the wall and by letting it flop against the floor; and she had bitten her lip.

My trips out of the house may have done me good but I concluded they appeared to stir up Sheila who became unsettled when she did not know where I was.

About 7.00 p.m., when Sheila was still down in the hall, we found her lying stretched out on the hard floor. She did not want to move so we left her there for a bit, covering her with a family blanket, which we had originally bought for her father. During that time she banged the floor twice with her right hand before agreeing to go back upstairs and get back into bed. She refused our offer of an ice pack to put on the bruising. We assured her that she was with her family and she began to joke with us.

Then she thought she was going to be sick. But later she felt well enough to have some ice cream and a piece of cheese for supper.

The Sixth Day - Monday, 31st MayWe had another disturbed night and her talk at times was irrational to me (though what she said made sense to her!) and she suffered mood swings and panic attacks. She was also disoriented, which was not surprising since she had not slept properly for some days. She wanted to know what day and time it was.

Just after midnight I gave her two Temazepams. She had about two hours deep sleep and then for the next hour she coughed and inhaled deeply and sat up. She had another temazepam at 04.30. It did not get her back to sleep. She was aware of her bruised right hand, which was getting knocked when she flung her arm back and caught the wall behind the bed. We talked and agreed that we needed to sort out her thoughts and to get her well again. 'The timing is right. We've got the time to do that' I told her.

The relaxation tape was on by this time, and she was saying 'Om', as it advised, to control her fears when a panic attack came on. She decided that since she had 'Om', Pat and me she was in good hands.

It was the Whitsun Bank Holiday and the neighbourhood was typically very quiet, as if asleep or unpeopled. Better cut the grass, I thought, wondering whom I might disturb. Once the mower had started I cut our lawn of buttercups and daisies. Then I did some deadheading of the climbing rose (always a soothing activity) before phoning Pat to give her our news. She was cautiously optimistic and felt Sheila could well be on the mend. We provisionally agreed to meet later in the week.

Jo, our second daughter, rang from Worcester and we brought her up to date. A friend, who was with us, kept an eye on Sheila while I gardened.

Sheila ate some apple slices and drank some milk. I made a list of things we might need, if we continued to have to nurse her: soup and chocolate; and for nursing some lip salve, and a bed pan. In the afternoon I sat at the little table in our bedroom and sketched and painted her while she dozed (having first asked me to guard her while she slept). I continued with a Pieta-style painting on some fine watercolour paper bound into a book Sheila had given me. I saw Sheila as going through a crucifixion-type experience and I painted rhythmical shapes that reflected a cross. Later downstairs I watched golf on TV: a relaxed Langer won at Wentworth. I sketched him and some trees.

That night I arranged to sleep in Ben's room (in order to get some sleep) and Rachel agreed to keep Sheila company. Having had a nap first, I stayed with Sheila from 10.00 p.m. till midnight. She was talkative and I sought to keep her calm. Rachel then took over. Sheila became noisy and restless (disturbed by the change in routine?). I gave her two Temazepams just before 4.0 a.m. and she slept for the next two hours. The meditation tape had also been on as an encouragement to relax and say 'Om'.

The Seventh Day - Tuesday, 1st June

My school/home diary simply says for Tuesday, 1st June, 'Same'. That means that Rachel and I were continuing to look after Sheila. But at the bottom of the section for the day, 'Need to get a night nurse'. We were increasingly concerned for Sheila and we were reaching our limits.

I hoped to contact Lynda (a close friend) who would help us. The plan was to work out a nursing routine (were we not doing that already?) which would give the two of us a break and we had to make sure Sheila knew what was happening and where I was. Thirdly we had, if possible, to get her to sleep at night.

More immediately we would need a visit from the practice nurse and it was time we organised a bath for Sheila. I would continue to use Ben's bedroom for sleeping. We still assumed that Sheila could be looked after at home even though we were beginning to need professional help. We were doing all we could to avoid her needing to go into hospital. The next thirty-six hours were to be harrowing.

Around 8.0 am, she was spitting and licking her lips. Her tongue was white and furry. She spat out a pill and a slice of orange that we had given her. Earlier she had stared at me for a time with her mouth open and then given me a kiss. Time to let the GP know how she was. I rang him and he advised giving her one stelazine at night (as agreed with Dr. Ahmed) and said she needed fluid.

I spent much of the rest of the day fixing up some help for that night. I was put onto Somerset Care and hired one of their staff, a trained nurse, to come and keep Sheila company throughout that night. The nurse would need access to the kitchen in order to use the kettle and to make coffee. Her fee (I think) was £60 plus VAT for the night. A good night's sleep for all three of us would be worth it and Rachel and I could pick up our duties suitably refreshed by a night off.

I also made contact with the practice nurse, who said she would call the next day.

Unfortunately Sheila was not to sleep much. She was fascinated by the nurse's name and called her Shaggy Baggy, which set them both laughing. Our visitor took this ribbing in good spirits but did get fed up when it continued. 'I may be baggy. But I am not shaggy!' she told Sheila. Our plan to have Sheila well looked after while we rested partly backfired, I suspect, because it introduced a threatening element of uncertainty into Sheila's existence. The presence of another person, a stranger, sitting in her room, a night lamp on beside her, presented a challenge and an intrusion to Sheila who both baited and engaged in conversation with her. It also confused Sheila and temporarily removed her sense of control, which in turn made it harder for her to relax and rest, if not sleep.

Another of Jeremy's paintings from the foot of our bed

Eighth Day –Wednesday, June 2nd. Admission into hospital

The next morning the verdict from the night nurse was that Sheila had not slept or been silent much and that she had never experienced anyone quite so disturbed and lively. I had been aware of some noise and activity during the night and not much else. But now listening to the report on the night - it was the gravity of that 'never' - I realised that Sheila might well be more ill than we had thought. Another person coming into the house can help one to get a fresh perspective.

We thanked the night nurse and she left. I then phoned Pat to update her and to clarify things. Rachel and I resolved to rotate the nursing duties, keeping Sheila as calm as possible and not exciting her. We would 'go with' what she wanted to do, provided no harm would come.

I also passed on to Rachel that Pat felt that Sheila needed to integrate various bits or experiences that she could not yet handle or absorb fully. We were urged to help our GP to see things from our point of view.

But events overtook us. I was just finishing some more mowing when the practice nurse came. She talked to Sheila and reported that she would be contacting the GP and also asking the Psychiatric Service to call. She was as good as her word.

Meanwhile, we had made contact with Peter, Sheila's brother-in-law, a retired consultant psychiatrist who had just got back from a holiday in China, and he had decided to come and see Sheila. He arrived on the 1.36 train from Paddington. He spent a long time with her.

The GP also called and doubled her medication. Then the community psychiatric nurse phoned to say that he was coming. When he had seen her and talked to Peter and us, we all agreed that she needed to be in hospital.

I do not think at this stage we had consulted Sheila or shared our feelings with her. Peter had to return to London that afternoon and did so, asking to be kept informed and promising whatever help he and his wife Jenifer (Sheila's sister) could give.

After much phoning and discussion in between calls the CPN found a hospital bed for Sheila. He had wanted her to go to Wells where the Unit was more 'open'. She would have been well looked after and her privacy would have been protected. He was concerned about her public role, that of a sister in the local hospital, being compromised or affected by her having to be a mental patient near our home. In the end Wells could not take her. But Park View, the closed and detached unit, could. So be it, I felt.

We let Sheila know that she needed skilled nursing and help and that we wanted her to allow us -willingly- to take her to hospital. I think we decided not to say where we wanted to take her. We felt that she would be more likely to co-operate if we did not tell her too much at that stage. To our relief, rather reluctantly and nervously, she agreed. Had she not, Ian would have had no choice but to 'section' her (or compel her to be admitted) and he did not want to have to do that. To Park View, then, by the 'back' route, he drove us.

Park View

It was about 8.30 p.m. when we reached Park View. A staff nurse took us into a waiting/reception room and took Sheila's details and made a list of the clothes and possessions we had brought. She was sensitive to Sheila's feelings and needs and also to her position in the local Health Service. It was quite difficult for Sheila to answer some of the questions and I had to help. I also tried to establish what was going to happen and how I could keep in touch and when I could visit. I remember being very struck by the staff nurse's comment that there was a very good chance that Sheila would make a full recovery; she had seen similar cases respond well to treatment and she added that they would do all in her power to get her well again.

My fears -and no doubt Sheila's as well – were that she would not come out of this 'madness' or mind state. I was to feed on that part of the conversation often and to share it with family and friends, and to need it in some of the dark days ahead.

At that stage, the admission interview concluded; I had to let Sheila go and allow others to look after her. So I kissed her and went to find Ian and he drove me back to my home and we chatted on the way. He, too, was able to continue the process that he and the staff nurse had begun of giving me a perspective on the illness and the place where she would be treated. He pointed out that Dr. Ahmed had to make a diagnosis and that things would be clearer once that had happened.

I thanked him and returned to give Rachel and D the news. An unutterable sadness came over me which even to recall can bring tears to my eyes. We had lost the battle to look after Sheila at home but at least she was in good hands. She needed help and she had not been getting enough sleep or eating enough.

So ended the first time I had really had to nurse or look after her at home. She was usually very healthy and strong. We were all embarking on what was to be another new experience - a long separation. All I could do was to trust and let her go in the hope that she would return.

The Next Phase

The next day, Thursday June 3rd, I visited Sheila in Park View. The journey took about ten minutes by car, was about six miles or so and was to take about thirty-five minutes on a bike. The building sits long and low, bungaloid, and faces back to the main building. Park View is surrounded by grass and is part of a park-like estate, which was due for re-development into a village. There's a drive straight past it - with parking spaces in front of the trees that fringe a huge stretch of lawn beyond which are cottages with gardens and young children playing in them. The large lawns form a terrace from which the ground slopes quite steeply away to the chapel, a children's unit and the nursing library to the west and to the main building and a training block to the south.

We were to look out onto the main 'lawn' and then walk out onto it, gradually spreading further, as Sheila's condition improved. We would watch people come and go and the children playing. Once it was a game of cricket, which fascinated Sheila.

But first I had to get into the Victorian building and see it by day. To do this you had to ring the bell and await a member of staff. He or she would unlock and let you in and possibly someone else out. You said who you were and who you had come to see and then usually called in at the office which was on the left once you had come to the corridor that ran left and right from there along the length of the building.

Sheila was in a side room, a single one. I cannot recall how she was except I know she was prescribed drugs which would help her to rest and sleep. A Dr. Mackenzie joined us and his concerns were to get a bit more of her history by working with me, representing her family and to decide where it would be best for her to be treated. I answered his questions about her and us and then he told me that he favoured her going to Exeter. I was firmly against that because it was too far and it would be difficult to visit her. (We were both still thinking, as had been the community psychiatric nurse, that she needed to be nursed away from the local group of hospitals in order to protect her identity.) I argued for the Unit in Wells, which was at least in Somerset and would be about three-quarters of an hour's drive away. Ideally I did not want Sheila to be more than a few miles away. There we left things for the time being. He was a junior doctor and could only make proposals that the consultant would have to approve.

I cannot remember whether Sheila was well enough to be involved in any of this. I was to visit daily for weeks and various patterns or trends emerged. I will generalise about these visits and her progress, describing highlights and low points and strong memories, running bits of various visits together in the interest of simplicity.

Those first few days Sheila was very ill, as if gone from us. She was in the end ward in the first bed on the right, usually asleep.

For much of the time I was with her I would sit by the bed while she slept or turned over. At others I looked out of the window. There was a wide view to the north, below the plateau the hospital is on, to scattered farms and houses with a local village beyond. I sketched one house in a group of trees, thinking if I cannot talk to her I can at least record a bit of the world not far from her. I wanted to do something positive and to shore up a bit of our collapsing world.

Ben, our son, rang on 3rd June and wanted me to get some flowers for Sheila. He would be coming home before he flew to the States later in the month and we discussed his funding needs.

Some Thoughts On The Treatment And Care Of Mental Patients

The staff nurse who had admitted Sheila had said that there was a good chance she would make a full recovery. I clung to that hope and shared it with those closest to me. She was to improve, though not without being very ill first and that hope, together with sensible and considerate nursing, must have helped her to get better bit-by-bit. But the way to recovery was pitted and not easy to travel on and we her family were left with little guidance, constantly having to feel our way as if we were blind. It was like being part of a Shakespearean tragedy.

The nature of mental illness is its unpredictability, its looseness of form or structure, its individuality. Compared to physical illness, which is usually dealt with once a diagnosis has been made, mental illness seems to be more fragile, fleeting and elusive. Others can argue from clinical evidence and case histories. What she and we as a family experienced were the uncertainties and delays, the fragmentation and slowness, of a service clearly stretched because of insufficient staff and resources and the frustrations and worries this produced in our friends and us. I am reasonably confident when it comes to talking to professional people about illness. Sheila is a highly intelligent and informed professional who could respond quickly, once well enough to do so, to the progress or slowdowns of her treatment. Without her brother-in-law to talk to (and there I was more fortunate than the average family member), I would have been in the dark, confused, frightened and angry.

The road to recovery ran like this. First there has to be a diagnosis by the busy consultant. Temporary medication plans are made based on the best interpretation of the symptoms. The consultant can only see the patient once a week, if all goes to plan, and sometimes once a fortnight, for he has a big caseload. He also goes to conferences and takes some holiday. An assistant, usually a registrar deputises, but this can delay any real progress being made, for example an alteration in the drugs being given. Getting the medication right is one of the keys to healing and recovery. But we found that even an adjustment in the dosage can take two weeks or more to happen. Slowness of service and response was a major fact of the service.

The same applies to the difficulty and struggles of the family who want to know what is happening either by wishing to talk to someone about medication or treatment or to get help and advice when they are nursing/looking after the patient at home and are finding things difficult. One cannot ring up the consultant to have a chat there and then. You can make an appointment but that is likely to be a week or more away. Junior doctors are even harder to contact, and etiquette discourages one from doing so. So apart from talking to nursing staff on the ward (and the relevant ones often seemed to be off duty), the first person to call is the community psychiatric nurse.

Getting hold of a community psychiatric nurse is not easy. Ours would answer the phone early on a Saturday morning, for instance, but as luck would have it he might be away for the weekend, on a course, or off duty. You feel left to your own devices when supporting a mentally ill patient at home. There are additional arrangements, such as support or activity groups; they are recommended when a person is well enough to attend.

That said, the staff we got to know did their best and were good people. What was lacking was some sort of briefing or booklet about mental health and some guidance on what to expect, a likely cycle of events or progress.

There was also evidence that the culture and ways of mental care are - inevitably? - sluggish and a bit sloppy in comparison with the rigour and briskness and more likely accountability of general hospitals' nursing and care. Sheila was restless and unsettled and untidy when ill but her room and the general ambience was depressing, often a bit grotty and not conducive to cheerfulness. I may be over-critical here but what her nursing care lacked was the sort of watchful liveliness to match the optimistic prediction of that kind and concerned staff nurse, who said she and the others would do all they could to see that Sheila got better.

The other surprise and sadness was the lack of continuity of staff at doctor and nurse level. Staff came and went, especially on the ward, and one key (nurse) worker was replaced by another. These changes, frequent and confusing, particularly for Sheila, must have delayed the sought-for healing. Blame the funding and resourcing of the NHS - yes, but remember how this person saw what such patchy provision did to his wife. As a nation we surely need to resource the care of our mentally sick far better and to inspire those nursing them with the worthwhileness of their task.

Sheila's Birthday

Sunday, June 6th was Sheila's birthday and it epitomised the change and the pain in our circumstances, though friends and family did all they could to alleviate our distress. I went to see Sheila early (soon after 8.0 am: the Ward was very good about letting one visit when it suited). Later Rachel and I went to see Sheila, who was sleeping and in no state to register what day it was. We then had lunch at a work colleague's home, relaxed there and returned to see Sheila. Back at home Jenifer and Peter came to tea and Rachel took some flowers out to Sheila. I got the grass cut (usually a weekend chore) and later cycled out to John and Andy's where we talked before walking round their dense and lush little wood, an Upper Cheddon paradise. That night my diary records that I 'didn't really sleep'.

There's a pattern and pathos in that summary. Every day I rang early for news from the staff about Sheila and visited as soon as I could. Time with friends and colleagues was always helpful and it was often then when I relaxed and joked. I continued my habit of meditating all through these months. On Sunday I would go to the 10.00am Parish Communion and I often found that the service had a cathartic effect and released tension that had built up during the week. Pauline and Sigurd and our Deaconess took us in hand so to speak and prayed for us. One Sunday after the morning service I went and talked in the Lady Chapel with them and the tears came, as they were to on other Sundays. I was amazed how at this stage of the week my control mechanism seemed to let go and my feelings took over.

That Sunday lunch (in Bishops Lydeard) was a beautifully served roast with several vegetables and a delicious homemade pudding. Rachel and I were treated to a celebration as if it was our day. Afterwards we had coffee in the garden and watched their rabbit, and on impulse I went and sat on the swing and became a child.

I gave Sheila a watercolour I had completed, painting some of it in our bedroom while keeping a watch on her. It was unframed but could be 'blue tacked' and so fixed up on a cupboard door or wall. It was of a woman being comforted by two others, one of who had an arm round her. At our painting class we had been asked to select a photo and to do a painting of it. I had been moved by this scene outside a court and had managed to catch some of the tenderness and pain of the original. Sheila had liked what I had painted. During her illness she responded to it more and more, talking about it, going up to it, wanting to know it was safe. It now hangs in our joint study.

Adjusting To Sheila being in Hospital

On the day after Sheila's birthday I returned to work, half-term being over, leaving Rachel at home, and started a new routine. I would ring the ward early and get news of how Sheila was and let the staff know when I hoped to visit. Then I would cope with the routine duties at school, going out to Tone Vale when there was a suitable gap. My colleagues at work were adamant that I put Sheila first and they insisted on covering for me, if necessary. Fortunately it was a relatively quiet time, exams were on - GCSEs but no Standard Attainment Tests were taken that year - and there were few visitors.

Sometimes I cycled to the hospital, which gave me some exercise and fresh air. I was prescribed Temazepam to help me sleep but advised that it was addictive. It certainly helped me to get better or good enough nights. My GP told me that it had been a very good sleep-maker for aircrews and others going out to the Falklands

Peter, Sheila's brother-in-law, continued to monitor things and he and I met Dr. Ahmed when he had a clinic at Park View at midday on 11th June. Dr. Ahmed diagnosed Sheila as suffering from a typical affective psychotic illness caused, he thought, by stress, confusion, negativism, and splitting off. He assured us that patients usually recovered from that sort of illness. Some of the indicators that she was suffering from that were her heightened state of awareness and her loss of touch with reality. When the mood disorder settled and as the medication took effect, then she would start to resume her normal ways of thinking and behaving.

That was reassuring news that I was able to mull over with Peter who dropped me back at school. He was a very good sounding board and friend. But Sheila was still very ill, not much in touch with us and we all hoped the medication would begin its work. Later I was to learn just how ill Dr. Ahmed thought she had been.

I cannot recall exactly when she moved from the small end ward to her own room but it was after a few days. My own notes, which now become patchier, record moments and memories.

Friday, 11th June:	on her stomach: complaining about 'too many captains here';
Sunday, 13th June:	a.m. she peeled an egg; called one helper 'Wilma'; p.m. she took my glasses gently, took my watch off. Polishing it in her slipper or 'Hush Puppy'. She sat on my knee, her head on my shoulder. She asked about the time and objected to the clock on the ceiling (a smoke detector) Apparently she had been taking her cards off the wall.
Monday, 14th June:	leave a book lent by a friend. Very loving and vulnerable. Playing with my watch and spectacles.

That night, I learnt, she had been in the sitting room where there was a TV She had been watching 'Casualty'. Another patient had been smoking (which Sheila never liked) and in her annoyance Sheila had thrown a chair at the window and broken a pane of glass. She had not been able to explain to anyone the connection between her thought and actions, nor, I think, had anyone on the staff tried to find out what had triggered that anger.

Tuesday, 15th June p.m.:	find Sheila in the sitting room with another person and wearing a white top. Signs of rage and frustration (it was not a room she could settle in). She moved chairs around, got rid of an ash tray, blocked someone's view of the TV 'None of that!' snapped the other person. She then meticulously wrapped up my three school books together with the TV's remote control, into a newspaper parcel. We chatted a bit. She found an old notice in my school diary and she read out some of the events on it and smiled. (No sign of my old watch, which Rachel had taken in for her that morning). She got noisier, then quietened, before

objecting to people talking in the corridor outside. M. comes in and apologises for disturbing us.

By now she was well enough to wander around and began socialising in a simple way with staff and patients. She was unsure of herself. She was on a fairly heavy medication. Her movements, remarks and gestures were tentative. She was exploring the whole business of relating to her new world in Park View and outside. She was not sure what to make of it or whether she wanted to go too close.

It was like watching a child begin to make sense of our amazing and quite strange world.

She was always pleased to see us and even when she was most affected, at her illest, I sensed part of her always knew that one of us was there with her, watching, waiting and supporting. The same was true of our going. She knew we were having to leave and she had to accept that. That instinctive knowledge was another candle of hope, an awareness that the visits did matter and were important.

Increasingly, especially at the weekends, I would join her in the canteen at breakfast, lunch or tea. The practice was for patients to do as much for themselves as they could and so join in with the life of the place. Disturbing others was not tolerated. Central to the recovery plan was being as self-sufficient as possible. Many were the meals I passed with her over a cup of tea or while she ate. Brief conversations would take place. I would relate my news.

Affected By Happenings Outside

Twice there were occasions when the outside world impinged upon Sheila's. They were both trivial incidents yet they raised questions and responses, the first she found both welcoming and puzzling, the second irritating, if not intrusive.

We were in her room and were looking out when we noticed some children coming up towards the nearby trees just across the drive that ran by the Ward. Children lived in the nearby staff houses and we were used to seeing them at play. But this time some three or four set up stumps our side of the trees and began a game of cricket. A girl was batting and there were whoops and cries, runs and chases, throws and appeals. Sheila was fascinated and could not take her eyes off them.

Was she reminded of the family tennis ball cricket games we used to play with our three children at her parents' house? Was she relating really to the play that was going on, wanting to be outside with them? I watched her new interest in the world she had come from.

The second demonstrated annoyance and wishing not to be disturbed. One morning an ice cream van drew up outside and began ringing its bell. Very quickly people started queuing. The sitting-room window was open and fixed

Jeremy's depiction of my 'dream' of crucifixion

a few inches at the bottom as it was a hot day and the sounds from outside came clearly into the room. Sheila was disturbed. She went to the window, said nothing, but trailed her left arm out of the open window and slowly waved a tissue from side to side as if to say, 'Go away! I don't like you or your noise!' One of the other residents, from outside, had a go at snatching the tissue from her, more in fun than earnest. Sheila did not like that, waited a bit, still flapping the tissue but in a more desultory way and then slowly and deliberately turned her back on the window and walked away. That turning away had 'A plague on both your houses' look about it.

The Beauty Of Walks

'Cooped up' was how Sheila felt it to be in Park View. The longer this went on the more she resented such restriction. It was difficult to accept since, as a ward sister she knew what her team were seeking to provide in order to aid their patients' recovery. As a patient one is forced to let go of freedoms and many choices. Now she was having to trust others and learn to wait.

The paradox of Park View was that whether one was a voluntary patient (admitted by your consent) or a sectioned one (there because two doctors felt you had to be) the staff were keen to let you come and go into the grounds and back into the building. If you were acutely ill, as Sheila was so judged, you could not leave the building. If you were being watched round the clock or observed every five minutes as Sheila was for a spell, you could not go out on your own. Someone could escort you outside for a short stroll, but this was dependent on the staff and the doctor's advice.

Sheila was allowed to be escorted outdoors, taken for little walks. I would call and we would walk in the grounds on our own, the two of us. There was the chance for her to breathe another air; moments of freedom; a shaking off - for a time - of the walls of the prison house. We could not go far and were expected to stay, at first, within the vicinity. Later we were able to roam more widely within the large grounds. But that June and July being in a park on a warm dry day with buoyant air, plenty of grass, big trees in leaf and shade under them and the sights and sounds of work outdoors was a restorative. Beyond Park View, over the village, to the Quantocks was a soothing sight; a draw and a reminder of better things.

On these strolls we branched out slowly, working a small patch in easy stages and then venturing a little further: first around the big field where the children had pitched their cricket wicket; then along the drive and down the hill over to the Nursing Library, to the Adolescent Unit and one day to the green surrounding the Chapel where there were tall trees.

We talked about further off things, our minds and thoughts freed of the confines of a small bedroom and we mused or reflected. I tried to cheer or encourage, as Sheila was able in her way to do for me. Also I tried to meet her impatience with trusting patience. We swapped news and bits of gossip.

Predictably a day came when someone we knew passed us in a car, waved or even stopped for a word (expressing surprise at seeing us). We also passed other couples, other walkers, one of whom we knew. These casual encounters were never long but nor were they easy. But they were part of a next stage of rejoining the rest of the world.

Home At Last

And so to July - family visits went on, daily in my case, similarly in Rachel's, briefly in Ben's before he flew to the States and from a limited number of friends. Sheila's enduring of the regime had to go on, too. Term was drawing to an end. There were sociable duties and celebrations. Staff and pupils came from the Jean Moulin School in Caen on an exchange and the school gave a party both for them and the Queen's College staff were also involved.

There had been other developments. Dr. Ahmed had ruled out the possibility of electric shock treatment, thank goodness. Medication was being relied on. A combination of two fairly powerful drugs, was now were causing some side effects. Sheila was eating better, sleeping better, getting exercise and going for walks, attending some classes or activities, such as enamelling and swimming, which she tolerated but could not enjoy. She was not up to reading more than a few words but she could write a note or brief letter. She was getting impatient to go home and making this clear.

The main blot or downside had been the occasions (countable on one hand?) when she had 'disobeyed' the staff or shown a fierceness which had led to two or more male staff manhandling her and putting her into a plain cell-like room near the front door, a 'padded' cell where they would stay with her until she quietened or leave her to 'come to her senses'. I never saw the beginnings of these incidents and, at the time, had only the staff's word to go on. I would ask Sheila what had happened and she was not clear why she had been so treated. As far as I could discern the staff had only put her in there when they felt they had no choice or when she had ignored their requests to move, say, from lying on the office floor or to stop doing something. It is difficult to be precise about the details. There were at least two occasions when I arrived and was told that Sheila was in the detention room.

I had to work out where the truth lay and to help Sheila to accept her punishment or correction and to encourage the staff to leave her or let her return with me to her room. I worried that this was happening but I had to accept it, albeit reluctantly. Later, I learnt that such treatment had deeply offended her and that she felt it was quite uncalled for. Had I realised that, I would have protested vigorously. But I doubt if the staff would have acted any differently when neither family nor visitors were around

In general she was making progress and she was allowed home for a few hours: for the evening on the 14th July, then again on the 16th, which was Jo's birthday. That weekend she was with us for most of Saturday (before going back for the night) and for most of Sunday, then on the Monday I got a phone call to say that she was being allowed home 'on leave' and so would remain at home instead of going back and forth. That excited us greatly and we could not quite believe it. On the 22nd she saw Dr. Ahmed and he officially discharged her. What we had been longing had come sooner than expected!

I told colleagues, friends, and family the good news and we adapted to having her back. Her delight at being back in her home with her own things, away from people having to keep an eye on her, in the company of her family, was wonderful to observe. She had never been away from home, other than during a holiday, for more than a week. The longest we had previously been separated had been just under two weeks in 1972 when I had walked the Pennine Way with a Sherborne School party. Under the joy of having her back with us, there were some anxieties, largely unaired, about whether we could cope.

It Was Not To Be Easy

From the start, thrilled as we were to have her home, we found that she was emotionally frail and in need of much support and care. Things had to be taken gently. After a valiant effort by us, after a month, she was re-admitted to Park View. Would a phased return have worked better, of say two or three days at home and two days back there? I doubt it.

The spell at home tested us to the utmost. It did not have the 'craziness', the sometimes manic activity and strain of the pre-admission week at the end of May. This time things went slower, far slower and cautiously. It was if we were expected to put Sheila together again, bit by bit, phase by phase. But no one initially talked us through how we were likely to find her or anticipated her fragility and vulnerability. We were on our own until we phoned the duty psychiatric nurse or Sheila went to the day centre for an activity or session. The three psychiatric nurses we consulted, who each called at some stage, gave us what help they could. But they were sometimes hard to contact. Weekends especially became long and empty times. We felt on our own, coping with a needy person, in unknown and difficult terrain; at times as good as abandoned by the medical services.

This becomes apparent as I run through a typical day. Sheila would wake early and need to be occupied lest she got restless and frightened. I got up and ran an early bath for her, trying not to disturb whoever else was at home. We spread the having of a bath for as long as we could. Passing the time of day was very hard for her. 7.30 was a bit soon for breakfast, so we would go for a walk by the river. Physically she was fit enough, fortunately and enjoyed exercise. It was a way of passing the time.

We then had breakfast, perhaps trying to do some of the quick crossword. Her appetite was good enough and she ate what we were accustomed to eating. Already we seemed to have been up for ages and there was still a long day ahead. The morning passed with difficulty and after lunch she rested but did not really sleep. We walked a bit more and did a brief shop (she found mixing with others quite threatening) After a cup of tea we tried a card game, watched a little television and had our evening meal. Then we talked to a friend or among ourselves, looked at some more TV and got ready for bed.

At bedtime she needed company, reassuring, staying with while she began to settle. She might have had a panic attack and so become upset. She was reluctant to take her tablets. Jo sat with her, mothering, comforting and helping her to relax and let go.

So a day would pass, stretched out like a taut rubber band, with its highs - the little achievements, each quite special - and its lows. It was like having a child again, an adult child who needed entertaining. This brought out our pity and tenderness. Sheila was not being obstructive or difficult on purpose. She could not relax into an activity for more than a short spell. Nor was she motivated to get on with an interest. She had not yet reached that stage of recovery.

We remained delighted that she was at home. It was what we all wanted for her- and we were determined to make it work. Had someone asked us, 'Suppose she has to go back into hospital'? ' Not if we have any say in the matter', would have been our reply. We tried anything that would help: Scrabble, walks, a little cycling, some shopping, drawing on our friends and outings in the car.

One early morning the two of us were walking by the side of the river, towards the sun, when I suddenly started seeing dazzling shapes. Had I been looking into the sun? These golden shapes stayed for a bit and then went away. I wondered if my sight had been affected, but no, a similar thing occurred on another walk, not long after. Again the symptoms went quickly. That was one of a few times then when I began to wonder if I was going to be able to cope. (One had been much earlier when I had said to Rachel, 'I think I may go mad'. 'No, you won't', she replied.)

In the summer school holidays families, and friends go away. When this is happening one has to be more self-sufficient and self-reliant. That August we found that few of our faithful local friends were about. That made us feel more cut off and increased our burden. I particularly would have valued being able to talk about the pressures on us and the stress we were under. One couple were at home and they would pop round for a chat. Later, when things were getting harder, they came and took Sheila home for lunch and then a walk in their paddock. She enjoyed their kindness and the break, but yet found it nearly terrifying. Would she be able to last the meal or would she have to ask them to take her home? How long could she manage away from her security and familiar things? She survived just, but judging by the way she talked about it afterwards, by the effort she had had to make, there clearly was a cost. We had to weigh up the risk and possible negative effects of doing something new against the possible advantages and gains.

Any major convalescence may well go haltingly - with advances and setbacks, good days and standing still days. Again we found ourselves entering the unknown and learning as things happened. We wished we had been warned that it might be a great struggle and been given some indication of the sort of likely progress. I plead that families need counselling in readiness for a member's return and convalescence.

However, I knew I could phone one of the duty psychiatric community nursing staff if I was really worried. I did so several times. The one I remember most vividly was one on a Saturday morning about 2.00 a.m. when Sheila was very low. She was getting panic attacks, which left her shaking and very unsettled. So I rang the duty person. This time I got him and he answered at once. He was marvellous and did not complain. He reassured us that we were doing the right things. No, he couldn't say when these attacks would stop but there would come a time when they did.

That was it! We had to turn over and try to sleep and then face what seemed like a very long weekend. What I did not tell him was that we were all getting tired and were wondering how much longer this could continue. Sheila was suffering, as were we. There must be an answer.

Sleep

Sheila had suffered from insufficient sleep back in May before she was admitted. She recovered after admission and settled into a better sleep pattern although nothing like as good as her normal one. Each morning, when I rang the ward before breakfast, I would ask what sort of night she had had. Often the reply would be, 'She woke early'. Gradually she picked up a better rhythm of sleep. But, among the many reasons why she wanted to come home, was the important one that she always slept best at home.

She did sleep better once she was back at home but she would wake early and need to be doing something. In Park View she would go to the office and chat to staff or someone would come and talk to her. At home she did not want to disturb us and so she went downstairs. In the dining room we had prepared some art materials, paper and an object or two for her to draw or crayon. She had a go but found concentrating on drawing or reading difficult so she could not stick at these activities for long. I may have pushed her into attempting to do these art activities against her natural inclination.

Like Sheila I reckon to sleep best at home. Sharing the same bed as Sheila is part of that good sleeping. Once she went into hospital my sleeping pattern went to pieces. I kept to our normal routine, of bath and bedtime. Also I would read Compline through and found strength in its lovely peaceful prayers and responses but I could not get to sleep. My mind was too active; I was not relaxed enough and I missed her - her presence, words and warmth. After still being awake in the early hours, I began to panic and to think, 'I can't cope. I will crack up if I don't get enough sleep'. But I also knew -from experience and common sense - that you can survive on a poor night's sleep; it is not the end; a poor night is often followed by a good deep sleep.

This was the worst, loneliest part of Sheila's illness and absence for me: the nights when I had to face thoughts and fears, awake when I wanted to be asleep and forgetting. Nevertheless, Sheila's suffering and torment, a veritable crucifixion, were far worse than I can describe and they outweighed by far my grim times. This aspect of her illness was particularly difficult and scary for me.

Reluctantly, on Sheila's advice I had consulted our GP and he had prescribed Temazepam, which worked well enough. But I knew I could only take the tablets for a short time, as they are addictive. I could not rely on taking tablets to get me to sleep. That summer holiday Sheila persuaded me to do without a tablet unless I had really had to (in which case the occasional half tablet was alright). I started getting better sleep, my own. We still had bitty nights, but we were able to support each other. My bottle of tablets was on top of the wardrobe now, available in reserve.

Expeditions

By day we were finding things to do together. The exceptions were the times when I went on my own to hit golf balls at the Haydon driving range and also to attend a church service. Jo, in her piece, mentions the place of golf and God in my life!

Gradually we went further afield. I remember two trips. The first was the time we decided to go for a cycle ride and we set off rather shakily up the cycle path towards the south. We were cycling to the school. After a while we emerged onto side roads and then, for the last section, had to use a middle lane before turning right. Only afterwards when we had stopped did Sheila let on how scared she had been, what a struggle she had had to keep going.

Balance was part of her difficulty when out cycling and no doubt the medication she was taking also hampered things. When going out in the car, she had to trust someone else to control our direction and speed and at first she was -understandably- edgy. I had to accept her nervousness and try to match my speed to her readiness as well as to road conditions.

One afternoon in mid-August we decided to visit the Leach Pottery near Muchelney. It was a pleasant country drive and not too long. The place was easy to find and we were soon chatting to John Leach and his wife though Sheila could only manage a few minutes. We liked his work and bought a small Tiv musical pot, based on a Nigerian design. It is glazed a lovely rich brown that turns to very light at the back and underneath, has a hole in one side and a matching hole in its sturdy neck and a tiny handle. It is a delight to pick up and has a rough feel.

We learnt that the Leaches had bought some land close by and had had it landscaped. We were welcome to visit it. We walked up a lane past a few houses and went through the gate into a few acres of new woodland, with paths round a largish pond. We explored the pond's edge looking out for flowers and birds and identifying the young trees. There is something soothing and calming about secluded inland water and we tried to imagine how the area would look in a few years' time. Sheila could only take a little of this and so we returned home. She had a go at blowing on the pot to see what music it emitted and drawing it. That outing, part of our gradual branching out, was our most ambitious and I admired the courage Sheila showed during it.

Back Into Hospital

Three days later, after we had discussed Sheila's needs with another community nurse, Sheila went off, as arranged, to the day centre (where facilities were on offer for those getting used to being at home again) for a couple of hours. Jo and I were aware that she was finding each day a struggle and that she did not seem to be progressing as much as we had hoped. She was having panic attacks and we had to give her more support, especially in the evenings. We were beginning to ask,' how much longer can we keep this up?' We had also discussed whether we should pay someone to be on call at night and so get a break ourselves. About midday the phone rang. It was the Registrar, Brian Kidd who had been at Ivor House that morning. He had talked to Sheila and had decided she needed re-admitting and that she was now going to Portia Ward. That was a blow for us all, a sad moment and it felt like a real setback, but the news did not come as a complete surprise.

Later that day we had to get Sheila's personal things to the hospital and meet the doctor who was admitting her. The apparent setback was more like a slip back, we came to realise, a pause in her improvement. But we quickly learnt that she was not going to stay in Portia.

Apparently (we have only had Sheila's account) she was deemed too disturbed for this 'open' ward. She was found carrying a bed end in a rather dangerous manner and the staff were not prepared to give her the benefit of the doubt or to wait and see if she repeated such behaviour. Sheila's explanation was that she was carrying out a perfectly rational act, which flowed from her perception (or hallucination) of what she had to do next. She would not have threatened or hurt anyone. She was sure of that.

That incident illustrates the gap between a person's own understanding of what is going on and others' perception of the meaning or likely outcome of their actions! But how can we know what is going on in another's thoughts? Aren't carers, the onlookers, bound to play safe or be cautious about allowing certain things to happen? How can we help a person talk about an hallucination? With hindsight and having heard Sheila's account of this, I would want to trust the patient more. I would certainly be able to trust my wife who is not violent towards others: blunt-spoken, yes, but never aggressive physically towards another (the exception would be if she was attacked). I would expect staff to ask her, or another person, 'Can you tell me why you were doing that?' and to listen to the answer before making any decisions.

Sheila and Jeremy

Back then she went to Park View, where she was to be given the same freedoms and regime as before. I think she was relieved to be back where she was known and with staff whom she knew (though there were staff changes going on all the time, which seemed quite normal to those running the ward). It had been clear that she was responding nervously to the Portia Ward's layout (a three- sided one, round a central void, on the first floor), and that she appears to have been thrown by its disparate 'open' style of caring for patients. The set up struck us both as very fluid and diffuse, with the staff office area some way from the dormitories or bedrooms. Did she unconsciously do something weird and strange in order to get herself returned to Park View where she could at least feel very secure, even if her return to there would seem like a backward step?

One can only speculate. Rachel replaced Jo, who went off for a well-deserved break, and she would see that Sheila got her daily visits and also let friends and family know what was happening. I made plans to go away for a short break.

Had Sheila not been ill she and I would have been camping once again with the school party near Stratford and seeing the plays for which we had tickets. I made arrangements to join our friends for the last few days of their camp but first I wanted to go to London to spend some time with Jenifer and Peter and then to see my father in Sussex. I needed a bit of looking after and some family support before tackling the camping, which was inevitably going to be a gregarious experience.

In London on the Sunday I was able to study Cézanne's oils and watercolours in the Courtauld Collection. I talked to Peter, my host, about my inability to get to sleep. 'Choose a book which appeals to you but turns out to be heavy and boring - and it will send you to sleep.' Good advice but it wasn't working too well for me, at that time! I talked to a close friend who helped me to get things into perspective and Peter, Jenifer and I went to see a modern version of 'Lysistrata'. In Sussex I brought my father up-to-date with the family's news and enjoyed his company. I also bought some golf shoes from the local golf club.

All these treats and pleasures had not till then been possible that summer. Rachel drove me to Stratford on the Wednesday and helped me put up our newish tent. It felt very strange being there without Sheila and not using our big tent. The adults had sent us messages and cards and accounts of the first few days of the camp and shown that they missed us. I got a warm welcome and was left to opt in or out to the chores and duties, as I felt like. That evening we saw a long and emotional 'King Lear' with Robert Stephens as Lear. It did move rather laboriously and many criticised his pacing and style. But I found it a powerful, authentic rendering.

I had wondered whether I could take 'Lear', a play that depicts a King going mad. But once the play had begun I was drawn into Lear's predicament and pitied him. Oddly enough the biographies I ordered from the Library, before Sheila's illness began, had both depicted madness. Peter Levi's 'Tennyson' would, I thought, teach me about verse writing. It did not go into as much detail about that as I had hoped, dealing with Tennyson's symptoms and bouts of depression or madness. Peter Ackroyd's 'T.S.Eliot' described how Eliot's wife Vivienne suffered from madness and how she was committed into an institution. All this could be seen as rather threatening to us and I read the books rather apprehensively, fearing that they might upset me or somehow be prescient. What I retained, with a thankful counter-pull, was the confident assertion of the staff nurse who had first admitted Sheila, who had said, 'There is no reason why Sheila should not make a complete recovery.' I had clung to that, both in the dark early days of her illness and again when I read those two biographies.

Park View Again

I have little recollection of my visits to Sheila on my return from Stratford that August. What became clear over the remaining weeks of her time in hospital was that Dr Brian Kidd, who was looking after her more and more, believed that she would recover and in due course get back to work. That is not to say that the other doctors were not trying their hardest. They played their part. But he conveyed a sense that he would not rest until she was better and he seemed to give her extra time and thought. It was also clear that Park View was a staging post this time. Sheila had managed at home for a month. She had made huge progress since the acute phase of the illness in June. At sometime she would be transferred to Portia where she would be prepared for her return home; that was the role of Portia's staff.

Equally we knew that Sheila was nervous about Portia. It felt a threatening 'world' to her and she would have to conquer her fears and distrust of the set up. The Park View staff, in particular her key worker, had to get her on an 'even keel' by getting her 'fit' enough first and also to build up her confidence so that she believed she could cope with life on Portia, having had a brief and unhappy first acquaintance with it. The Park View team would advise the doctors on Sheila's readiness, bearing in mind that they would want to be doubly sure, this second time, that Sheila was ready for Portia.

The decision was made on the 2nd September for Sheila to transfer the following morning. Her key worker was closely involved in the handing on and Rachel was able to assist by carrying some things and by staying for the first few hours until Sheila was reasonably settled.

The Final Phase

My job was keeping me busy and there was little time for reflective writing. I have strong memories of certain things and some happenings but the general background information has gone. Once again we established a pattern to our visiting and support. Rachel would also visit, in addition to offering any back up and helping liaise with friends and family about Sheila's progress and good times to visit. We were aware that the crisis had long passed, that Sheila was going through a setback rather than relapse, which helped us to relax, let go and leave things to the staff and doctors.

My visiting tended to be in the early evening or later around 8.30. There were two main meeting places. Portia was a rambling set up, round three sides of an enclosed courtyard and on the first floor. At first we used to talk in a little cupboard of a room. We could chat in a sitting room, where the television might well be on and others were watching it or playing a game or doing a jigsaw. We preferred to be on our own, so we huddled in the box room that was used as a store. It felt a bit like playing truant to be in such a confined space but it was private.

Then a member of staff told us about a big sitting room downstairs off the main corridor. This was like a room in Hestercombe House, with a high ceiling and comfortable furniture. It was used as a waiting room by day for people waiting to see a consultant. At night we usually had it to ourselves.

We would exchange news and I would pass on any letters of interest or messages. We might look at the quick crossword. Usually it was a matter of comforting or encouraging each other. Sheila was increasingly dissatisfied with being on Portia - a good sign, I thought - and complained to me about this person's habits or the routine of the ward, the tensions and irritations of sharing one's day with people you did not know or had not got much in common with and who were probably as restless as you, as unsettled by their drugs and as keen to get out. Partings became harder as the days went by. I had to get back to do a bit more work before bedtime. Sheila found the time dragged cruelly.

It was better when we could walk in the grounds, round the former playing fields, doing a half mile or so circuit: down the drive towards the lodge house and road, then round the field, back by the second set of grass pitches near the pavilion and tennis courts, passing by some mature mixed trees and seats and then back via another lane until the main building loomed up on our left like an oil tanker above a dinghy. The space, fresh air and freedom helped to revive our sense of life's goodness and gave us some exercise as well as a better appetite for the next slice of our current routine. Always attracted by the visual, I would point out trees I liked and things I had noticed while Sheila would remind me of some practical matter at home, as well as greeting those we might see or pass. Had the ward been in the town we would have had a much noisier and less soothing walk.

Better still, the time came when Sheila was allowed out of the grounds, say for an hour's run in the car and then home on a phased and increasing basis. She came home for two hours on 6 September, which was three days after she had moved to Portia and again on 9 September. On 13th September she was walking with us in our local river-canal countryside. The following Saturday she was home for the day and I made a note on 22nd September that she was making good progress. The following weekend she was allowed to stay the night at home. The drawn-out spells that I have been referring to occurred between these outings and periods of leave.

My sister, Julia, visited us at that stage and although she could not know what Sheila had already gone through and therefore acknowledge the progress she was making, she was able to talk to her and consult her about nursing matters in the United States. Seeing Julia was a great help for me and it meant I had her company for a few evenings. Apart from Julia's visit local friends continued to play an unobtrusive part. There were people I could talk to at school and from home. My sister-in-law, Jenifer, and her husband Peter continued to monitor how things were going and to give practical support. One friend dropped round with pears from her garden, another made a pudding.

About now Sheila complained of frightening dreams and nightmares, which unsettled the poise established on the previous days and also of bitchiness and sheer bloody-mindedness on the part of one or two women patients who called her names and saw her as a 'snob'. Nothing like this had occurred till then. It was yet another reason for Sheila feeling impatient to be discharged and come home.

We made an outing or two: one was to drive to a village and on up into the Quantocks, where we had tea at the cafe at the crossroads. It was good that we were going out together to do an everyday thing. We were picking up some pieces of our usual life. Having other people around was a threat to Sheila and she could only cope with so much. But she was managing with help; and that was what mattered. Back on Portia she still found the time dragged uncomfortably. She could not settle to any one thing for long. She tried knitting and reading. She could watch TV. For the rest she had to cope with herself; her thoughts and fears; the apparent desert ahead of dragging time. There was little we could do to change that other than help her with words of comfort and our non-verbals and so help her to believe that she would get through that phase.

Early in October she had felt well enough to accept an invitation to lunch - on her own - with friends who lived nearby. In fact she was down, worried that she had reached the end. She admitted to them that she was feeling as if she was going to die. Her medication, she felt, was slowly poisoning her. Unknown to us the husband, a doctor, had phoned the ward and warned them. We knew that she was worried, for she had also told us. We took her back earlier than had been agreed (there was a standing arrangement that this should be done if she was not coping). That night and the next day were anxious times for her and us. Was she going through a new crisis, a serious development, or was this merely a slip back? We could not be sure. She was tough, determined and a fighter. She had so far proved a powerful survivor. But people surprise you and one must not take someone for granted or believe that you know what is going to happen. Best to be cautious and humble about them and their future.

Fortunately she rallied, thanks to very prompt and skilled assessing and altering of her medication by the duty doctor. There was a lull in her going out for the next week, understandably, for the staff wanted to keep a closer eye on her. But she came home on 10th October and she made good progress - so much so that I arranged a short four days holiday with a friend over half-term, confident that she was in good hands and expecting her to be coming home 'for good' not long after that! She visited Ward 7, the ward she had been running, on the 17th October and the staff were very pleased to see her. That took place during a weekend at home.

I returned on 28th October, after a very enjoyable golfing break in Cornwall, to find Sheila home, discharged, well and mightily pleased to be out of Tone Vale. What a moment for us all! Two days later we visited a cousin in the countryside west of Tiverton and spent a happy day talking, catching up, and helping them on their small holding. It was like old times to see Sheila having lunch with relations and joining in with normal life. But there was plenty of adjusting to be done. The great thing was that she was home and could take her time; decisions about the future could be made as were necessary.

8. RACHEL'S CHAPTER

Monday, May 17th
The arrival of myself and D[1].
You suffer from insomnia, failing to sleep properly and waking very early. Your mind is active.

Monday, May 24th
You get no sleep all night. You are over-working, insisting that you need to be busy.
There are unusually high levels of stress on your ward[2]. There is a new coffee machine on the ward, which means that you have increased your caffeine intake. There is a family history here – Jenifer avoids all caffeine.

Tuesday May 25th
You return from work unable and unwilling to make decisions – e.g. over supper and what to cook.
You have recently discovered art. The self-portrait, which you paint for Ben's 21st, brings many different feelings and emotions to the surface. Given your age, 51, menopause may be a contributory factor.
You are determined that I should get to know you properly. You describe your need to be in control frequently, repeatedly referring to and quoting Jung. You are aware of the approaching half-term break, a good time to let go with holiday on its way anyway. You are also conscious of me being around and able to help on the domestic front.

Wednesday, May 26th
The first day of sick leave.
At breakfast you appear very wobbly and nervous, looking so pale and tired. You are lost in a tormented world of your own. 'You can put it down to the menopause' you say. I go ahead with an arranged trip to see Maggie in Southampton, at the psychology department. D joins me and we collect Naomi. Late that evening we return to Taunton to find friends visiting Mum and Dad. There is a strange, tense atmosphere. I learn that you've had a panic attack over my late return, partially exacerbated by the news seeping through of a plane crash on Southampton's M3. A call to the police has been made. The friends

---

[1] A friend, with whom Rachel had been travelling and who stayed with us for the duration Ed.
[2] I was a Sister in charge of an acute medical ward with a chest specialism at that time, Ed

Rachel

leave promptly.

This shocks me. It is so unlike you to worry. What is going on? In fact all day I've worried about you. What is wrong? I'm convinced it's my being at home with D as well. I conclude, before leaving Southampton, that we must leave Obridge.

Dad has a word, filling me in on the day and your appointment with Dr B. Sleeping pills have been prescribed. Something is terribly wrong with you. It hurts to see you suffering.

Thursday, May 27th

Dad goes to school until 2.30pm. You rest in bed, with me looking after you.

For the first time since all this began, you talk openly to me about what is occurring.

Yes, you admit, it is to do with my presence. I have triggered off all of this. But...that is all. You tell me you 'knew' a breakdown was on the way and it's mainly connected with childhood traumas. A certain amount of weight is lifted from my shoulders. You quote Larkin's 'parents' poem[1] to me.

We sort out Sainsbury's finances. It takes $1^{1}/_{2}$ hours due to your heavy weariness. You are still really unwilling and unable to make decisions. (Role-play is initiated, during the course of the morning, at your suggestion. I find myself being taught how to nurse and having to call you 'Mrs Harvey'. Lesson 1... 'Turn the patient's pillow frequently'. This role-play greatly appeals to you, is taken very seriously by you and yet seems to amuse you as well. You focus totally on teaching me. It absorbs you. When I happen to indicate that the first initial of my other name and D =R&D= Research and Development, you are very taken and organise the start of a 'Research and Development' File. You are very pleased and delighted with this finding. A friend calls in, wanting to know about the next Book Club. He learns Mum is ill. Maggie, his wife, sends a card. In the evening we all watch some comedy show. You laugh hysterically. Is this a release of nervous energy? You announce that you believe caffeine is the problem and will be avoided from now on.

One of my great aunts returns a call made by you earlier in the day. You need to know the truth about your father.

Friday, May 28th

Ben phoned to discover Mum unwell and the trip to France is off. I have found that the relaxation tape helps, with use of 'Om' during panic attacks. George (the voice on the relaxation tape) has a calming and reassuring voice. I helped you to dress and instructed Pam and Ray (domestic help) to go home and await a call from Dad. Pam is the last person you can face right now.

We collect Dad from school and drive on to Dr B's. I wait while you both go in. Afterwards you are drained of all physical energy. Dad and I finally get you

---

[1] 'They fuck you up your Mum and Dad............Philip Larkin.'Ed.

to the sofa in the hall. France has been cancelled. Dad is hoping you'll be okay for a few days in a B&B at the end of half term. Later you walk alone from the bedroom to the kitchen. Fits of real, sudden energy are interspersed with complete fatigue.

Saturday, May 29th

I heard you screaming last night, a panic attack?

Today you are elated by your discovery of a way to save Bosnia and the World. Pat[1] is here for most of the day talking to you. Suddenly you are three and a half, and Peter Rabbit is present. You skip through the house playing Flopsy bunnies. You need massive reassurance.

Sunday, May 30th

I allow you to phone Jill, as you want to speak to her. Hear you announcing yourself as 'Sister here'. It's followed by 'I need massive reassurance'. The phone was promptly removed when you began shouting 'bugger off'. Syddy called back and asked if he could help.

After lunch Dad goes over to the Peacockes' for a break. In his absence I find myself (four or five times) trying to stop you from running into the garden. It's a huge task restraining you, even with D's help. You experience such great physical energy, ecstasy and enjoyment. D panics during the struggle, this unnerves you, seeming to make you more aggressive and determined to reach the garden. This you succeed in, running and jumping before collapsing in an exhausted heap. Drained of all energy we get you inside. 'The only way I can contain this is with Dad here', Mum tells us. I call him. I've learnt calmness is the essence, the best way to assist you in remaining calm.

Now you are a tiny mouse, small and frightened. You openly discuss your symptoms as if partaking in a meeting on your ward. There is a new pattern today. Rather alarmingly you are now hitting yourself. You were thumping the hall floor earlier, bruising your hand and hitting your hands together too. You talk out loud all day as if Pat is here and listening. There are phone calls from Jo, Jenifer and Peter, who are told the latest. Dad's low today and struggled to eat supper.

Monday, May 31st

You have a very badly bruised right hand. You need 24 hour nursing, and therefore someone with you nearly all the time. You need me (or Dad) to say 'Om' very quietly. This calms you down if you are having a panic attack. You are sucking your thumb and saying 'I'm only a very tiny and quiet mouse'; talking about your father's father and his suicide and various cousins. You prepare for the arrival of the family, which isn't planned. You are hitting your face. This is a new area of concentration after hurting both hands yesterday. You are also clasping your mouth with both hands and tensing the whole body up at the

---

[1] My Psychotherapist from therapy which 'ended' a few years before, Ed

*Rachel's photos of me taken in
Park View*

same time.

Dad had a break today, as he's very tired. He slept in the spare room last night, so I camped out on the floor in your room. You are fairly quiet and still after yesterday's energy, with a lot of whispering to yourself, often about Benjamin Bunny. You are adorable when playing a happy child. Jo phoned, I don't think I sounded all that reassuring.

Tuesday, June 1st

A big concern is felt, as you're eating so little, nothing yet today. You rejected a segment of orange. You are swallowing little fluid, spitting or coughing up most of it.

Dad is very upset. He called Lynda. We can't cope between us. Is Hospital inevitable? You are no longer using 'Om' and have staring, distant eyes. 'Smelly old Badger'[1], you say and are talking about twins often. Who is your twin you ask?

Dr B arranged for a District Nurse to phone Dad – but not visit in person. You are advised to get on your feet as often as possible, even if just to go to the loo. In the afternoon Lynda arrived to give us a break. As she left I had a word. She believes this could go on for months and is serious. Her way of nursing you is to pursue your thoughts and go with the flow. It was a relief to chat to her. I find her good at saying the right thing.

Dad's arranged a nurse to look after you during the night. Which she does from 10 pm to 8 am. You are noisy and energetic all night, misbehaving generally and get no sleep. On announcing to Jeanette that you've nicknamed her 'Shaggy Baggy' she replies, 'I may be baggy but I certainly am not Shaggy!'

Wednesday, June 2nd - Crunch Day

At 5 am I take in milk for you and tea for Jeanette. You seem even more disturbed; making me worry that Jeanette was a bad thing. Hockey sticks on my sweatshirt upset you, presumably reminding you of school.

Once Jeanette leaves, you calm right down, remaining still despite an over-active mind. You continue to talk out loud and today there are many tears as well. You are very sensitive to smell, rejecting an orange because you don't like its smell, but rejecting drinks less and successfully having a Complan drink. There is less hacking up and spitting out of phlegm.

Your face twitches and you grab it, as well as pointing and drilling with your right hand, which all cease this morning. You are much calmer, in fact miles away in your thoughts, busy recalling and saying things such as:

'This is a creative room'

'Horribly medically sharp' (smell)

'We are the royal family'

'And I can and I will. And he can and he will.'

---

[1] A reference to my father, Ed.

Your thoughts move rapidly.

There is an actual visit from the District Nurse before lunch. Merely listening to you speak was enough to convince her that the 'simple doctor' needed to do more. She basically initiated the professional move to get you hospitalised. At lunch Peter – my uncle by marriage - arrived from London. He too needed little time with you before disappearing to convince Dad that you need to be in hospital for sedation.

Dr B visits next, prescribing stronger medication to make you sleep. Also the psychiatric nurse, Ian, arrives. Dad mistakes him for an insurance salesman! Ian uses his portable to arrange a bed for you. I remained with you upstairs while Dr B, Ian and Peter talked to Dad in the kitchen. Peter kept me from feeling stranded by giving regular updates. You seem unaware of what is going on as I pack a bag for you. Your psychotic, manic and hyperactive behaviour continues. You're to go to Park View, the Intensive Treatment Unit. Ian drives you and Dad there.

I can't get Ben on the phone, but manage to update Jo. We both cry.

Thursday, June 3rd
First thing Dad phones Park View to establish how your first night went. You have got some sleep during the night. This morning you are quiet and withdrawn – not speaking to anybody. Dad and I visit you in the morning. I feel apprehensive as to how we will find you. You look sleepy and distant. Presumably as a result of the drugs your bottom jaw has dropped. Due to a few days of eating so little you have visibly lost weight and look weak and frail. Diminished, too, by being the only patient in a large room. It is all very upsetting.

The staff have failed in their attempts to feed you. I have a go and manage to get you to drink some Ribena and eat some toast. Meanwhile Dad talked to Dr M. As it's all happened so fast your recovery should be fast. Tomorrow an ambulance is due to take you to a unit in Wells. Dad's pushed for Wells in preference to Exeter.

Dad finds Ben in and gives him the news over the phone. Mrs C (Nurse Manager) is informed you won't be back on Monday. Apparently she isn't surprised, but very understanding.

At 4pm I take over from Dad at Park View. You are chatting and definitely perkier again. Generally you are still in bed. I get some photos of you, as I'm sure you will want to know about it one day. You are still simply refusing to eat properly. You are saying things such as:

'Lets have some fun with this one for a while'.
'I need time to get my energies together/back'.
'Take time to gather myself'
'I want to be at home'.

You are certainly aware of where you are despite not communicating directly with anyone. You did say, 'Hello Darling, and how are you?' when I first arrived, before your thoughts moved on immediately. You growl loudly, kick the bed covers off and clothing. You seek air which you need lots of. Air is a recurring theme. You've also started massaging your cheeks with your fingertips and touching your left ear constantly. There is a skin rash around your ankles. The new phrase is:

'She-She Bear. He-He bear'. Jo is staying with an uncle and aunt for the night.

Friday, June 4th

At breakfast Dad phones the hospital and tells me that you had a fairly good night, are screaming a bit this morning and have been bathed and dressed. He visits you for an hour. Your watch is missing, stolen? You are apparently noisy and no different really. Peter phones, wanting to know if there's a diagnosis yet. Dad lets the Andersons know that you've been hospitalised. Pauline visited you and called in at home afterwards to let us know. She found herself being called 'Pat' and needed a nurse to help prevent your hyperactive doings. I arrived at 4.15 pm to discover you had only had four hours sleep last night. There is no official diagnosis still. More, and different, medication is required, but everything's on hold as consultants are off for the weekend. Vicky is looking after you. I find you calm, but overall there is no improvement. This is concerning the professionals, so Wells will wait.

You rock yourself, mumbling but not talking loudly or continuously today. There is one other person in the room, a young woman who repeatedly tells me she's 'haunted'. At one point you signal me to keep quiet. Later on you suddenly sit up, look at me, and say 'Ben' with your arms out before lying down.

Dad popped out in the evening to see you, there is no change. The team are trying you on new drugs tonight. I phoned to let Syddy and Jill know the latest. Pauline got in touch expecting Mum and Dad back from France. So I duly updated her.

Saturday, June 5th

Dad learns that you slept between 11pm and 4/5am last night. Your watch has turned up, the culprit discovered? Jenifer and Peter visit you. During their stay your key-worker Linda phones Dad to ascertain his permission for passing on the diagnosis to Peter. Next, Jenifer and Peter arrive home, Jenifer is visibly upset. They have a list of things you need. Peter is adamant that you should be physically examined, although this poses problems due to your restlessness. You are seriously ill so there is no hurry to move you to Wells. He has a chat with Jo, who phones from our Uncle and Aunt's, reassuring her regarding all that is going on.

Jenifer managed to get you to drink some 'pink drink' (unbeknown even to Jenifer and Peter). You had half, but still hardly eating. Dad feels he was not given sufficient professional advice during the time we were looking after you. There was a distinct lack of support.

In the afternoon Dad takes some clean clothes out to you. You sleep peacefully for most of his visit, turning over a couple of times, mumbling a few words. The good news is you now have your own private room. After supper I visit. Vicky informs me blood samples taken are currently being tested. I make myself comfy in the high-backed armchair by your bed, one of two. I take a couple more photos as you lie quietly on your bed. I still can't believe what has happened, things have happened too quickly to catch up with and contemplate. Maybe thinking about it is too upsetting, better just to function and cope.

You ask me 'Where am I? Who am I?'

You cough frequently, moving from side to side on your bed. I observe the small bruises on your arms, all too usual these days. You rub your closed eyes and throat. Your eyes look tired, distant and staring. Your ankle rash has disappeared. It was probably an allergy to one of the drugs. Roger, the vicar, visited after I left.

Sunday, June 6th - 51st birthday
It's your 51st birthday. Dad contacted Park View to discover you'd had a good night's sleep, even nodding off prior to the night staff undressing you. Not wishing to awake you they left you.

Dad took cards from Jo and Ben in with him. You concentrate for a while on him reading the contents. But really you are unaware that it's your birthday. The two of you hug and kiss a lot and you try to buck him up when he's upset. Dad goes on to Church. Tom Preater phoned sending love and best wishes to you and Dad.

Dad and I together take more cards out to you later. I put them up on the wall. You've had a bath and are in shorts and a short-sleeved blouse. After consuming only three mouthfuls of roast beef first course, an apple pie with custard is eaten quickly. Suddenly you've acquired a sweet tooth! You sit on Dad's lap on and off. Still talking about 'She Bear' with big staring eyes. But you are shouting less and not talking so constantly. You are much quieter.

Dad and I go to the Peacockes' for lunch. On our return to Park View you drink something and eat a few strawberries. Jenifer and Peter visit you and then come home for tea. Peter feels sure you should remain at Park View. I spend an hour with you from 6.30 delivering some flowers from the Reimers'. Andy and Janet Painter phone today for updates. I manage to chat to key-worker Linda who does not think Mum will remember any of this. All the more reason for me to keep a diary and take photos. Linda herself was unable to visit her Mum when she went crazy as a result of oxygen treatment for pneumonia.

You have soup for supper. You need a blanket and dressing gown, as it's chilly. You refuse to go somewhere (loo?) with Linda, staying on your bed. You move around and groan at one point giving the impression you're in pain. Jo phones to find out how you are.

Monday, June 7th

Dad has returned to school after half-term. Andy visits you at Park View in the morning. After a good night's sleep you are still quiet and sleeping while Andy visits. Dad comes home for lunch and phones Park View. Dr Ahmed, the consultant, is expected to visit you some time.

I visit you in the afternoon. You start disappearing under your bed, lying on your back and clinging to the bedsprings, reluctantly emerging once the curtains in your room are drawn. This is a new pattern of behaviour. You eat a few mouthfuls of mashed potatoes and all of the rice pudding. You also drink milk happily. The staff give you another tablet, a sedative? Later you are quiet, as you lie awake on your bed with your hands covering your ears, objecting to the loud noise levels around your room, for example coming from the TV room? The door of the larger room, you were first in, always slams. Physically you look thinner again with a gaunt, pale face. There is more bruising along your right arm.

Before the end of my visit you've begun muttering and groaning, rapidly shaking your right hand and a pointed index finger. You are also putting two fingers in your mouth. I manage to get you to drink only a quarter of a mug of Complan. I felt that you registered my presence less than ever.

After supper Dad visits you. He is still unable to sketch you, as you don't remain still for long enough. This evening you are quiet. No psychiatrist will visit you until Thursday Dad learns.

Tuesday, June 8th

Lynda visits you in the morning. Taking grapes with her, which she skins and de-pips. You relish two, gobbling them down and then say 'No'. Lynda feels not enough is being done. Sure, the Staff has managed to get you to sleep due to drugs, but you're barely drinking enough let alone eating sufficient. A diagnosis and plan of what to expect is required. Peter phoned us to say he feels it is time the doctors pulled their fingers out. So, he has arranged to see Dr Ahmed and Dad at Park View on Friday. The concern is mounting. Peter's also phoned Linda your key-worker.

Pip, from Mum's hospital, phoned offering help. I explained that Mum's in another hospital. We left it so that I can contact her or Sue P should they be required to visit. Probably better if they stay clear.

In the afternoon I drive out to visit you. Informed by the staff that they have removed your bed, as they were worried about the damage you could inflict upon yourself. You are constantly on and off the bed, frequently clinging to the bedsprings underneath and curling up in a ball. But the effect of a mattress only on the floor is somewhat distressing, conjuring up prison cell associations.

You appear unaware of my presence. I held your head, supporting it while

I fed you a cup of Complan. I hear you say 'Alright Darling' as I leave. Prior to my departure some man, presumably a doctor, just walks in (ignoring me completely) and asks if you object to going to the general hospital for various X-rays or would you prefer the private one? You don't really respond. Again your arms seem to have more bruises. Your eyes remain shut most of the time and you are weak and shaky.

In the evening, phone calls from Uncle Simon and John Rose, Dad himself phoning Keith and Helen. Dad visits you after supper. You've consumed soup for yours. Spend some time in the garden, but are unable to walk in.

Wednesday, June 9th

Dad visits you in the morning to discover you've had cornflakes for breakfast and drunk some Build Up. Apparently during the night you chatted to Tracey, one of the night staff, telling her about your training and qualifications, a good sign. Apart from singing about Noah's Ark, you talk little during Dad's visit.

I visit in the afternoon to find that you've already left for the general hospital for routine head and chest X-rays. Maggie tells me there's no real change, but perhaps you are eating more. I sort out the clean clothes that I have bought for you. Await your return in the ambulance, but at 4pm you're still not back, so I reluctantly head homewards. At 5.45 Pauline gives me a lift; it's her first visit to you. I find you safely back from the trip, not saying very much at all, weeping on and off. You've eaten soup and chocolate cake for supper and drunk some Complan.

You let Pauline hold you. Now you're off at the end of the bed huddled in a ball. Pauline and I get you back on the mattress. You wave your arms and repeatedly poke your throat. Your room feels very warm. To me you look the most unsettled and distressed I've seen you for a while. This tests the faith I have to have in the Park View team. What is going on? I need to see some signs of progress. At one point you suddenly open your eyes, look at me and give me a huge smile. Then once you are stiller, seemingly calmer, we sense it is time to depart. It's never easy, I always feel as though I'm abandoning you. It's not true of course.

I manage to have a word with the nurse who escorted you today. Apparently your face lit up as you arrived and you laughed! They carried out several tests on your head and chest areas. Now we await results. You were very quiet and patient during all the long periods of waiting around, very disruptive for you, but you appeared to cope well at the time. The reaction occurred later back at Park View. There is no change.

Thursday, June 10th

Early this morning you had no visits. At lunchtime Dad called in to discover you are weepy and in need of affection after not such a good night. Dad thinks you are lonely. Dr Ahmed has visited you. His efforts at extracting information failing as you don't really talk to him. He's altered your medication as from now. This change will probably bring out more emotions. You manage to sit up and eat a fairly good lunch. You keep your hands in your pockets.

Later in the afternoon I arrive to find you very weepy initially. Coax you into opening your eyes and seeing me. You grin at me. I check that I am not upsetting you and you don't indicate that you would prefer me to leave. You are now still and quiet, lying on your side, having rolled off the bed once. The Staff say that your weeping is a good sign. I failed to pursue the reasons for this. Presumably as it releases bottled emotion and pent up feelings - therapeutic.

Now you are gnashing your teeth, rolling around occasionally and wafting your arms about slowly as you lie on your back. Chattering teeth. You are crying on and off, sometimes tears fall, sometimes they don't.

A late evening visit from Dad, during which he does not feel in touch with you. You are quite active. Possibly you are on no sedation currently. You look younger today.

Friday, June 11th

At 9am I phoned Park View for an update. Spoke to the Sister, and she put me off visiting as you are in a good deep sleep. In fact she feels it is the best sleep you've had since arriving. You apparently fell asleep at 1am. At 11am I phoned Park View again and was again put off visiting you. This is despite the fact that you are awake. Fair enough you're in a drowsy state but I don't like being told I can't visit you when it's obvious I'm being fobbed off with weak excuses. Why do I feel annoyed? Why is a feeling of distrust and suspicion towards the staff with me? If they very reasonably feel you should not be visited because it stirs you up and disrupts you, I want to be told directly. Who do they think they can kid, patronising *-?!*s, (sods).

I take the car up to the school for Dad. At 1.30 he meets Peter and Dr Ahmed at Park View. The fantastic news is, and this is an incredible relief, there is absolutely nothing physically amiss with you. All the test results are back. Ahmed's diagnosis is that you have an atypical affective illness, in other words a mood disorder as well as a 'nervous breakdown'. You are to start a new course of sedation and anti depressants. [1] The results will be observed over the next two weeks and then, if there is no change, electric shocks will be used to stimulate part of the brain. Dad finds Ahmed an excellent doctor and trusts his diagnosis. Peter too, believing we'll have the normal you back with us soon. Your comment is 'Too many captains'.

3.30pm and Lynda visits you. At first you are huddled in a ball on the floor. She is encouraged by your recognition of Dad, Dr Ahmed and Peter. Also you ask Lynda, 'Where am I, what am I doing?' Like me Lynda feels you are aware of everything. She also observed that your general smell is better.

---

[1] Actually Chloral Hydrate -a sedative - and Thioridazine – an antipsychotic. Ed.

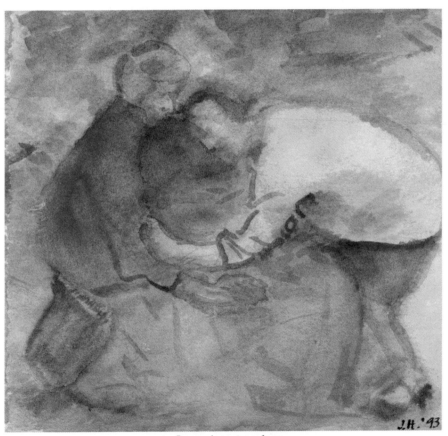

Jeremy's watercolour
'comforting in intense suffering'

Saturday, June 12th

At 9am I phone Park View enquiring if it is a suitable time to visit. You're asleep, but about to be woken and given drugs. Now, due to my visit your bath is delayed. Your key-worker Linda greets me at the door with the news that you're flatly refusing to move this morning. You have said nothing and not even opened your eyes. Instead you are busy shaking your arms violently and rapidly. You are also hitting your watch. You stretch out your right hand as though pushing something away. 'Sneeze' is uttered. All of this indicates no change in your condition to me. I make you open your eyes. They're all sleepy and drugged looking. I give you a hug. Throughout your visit you hardly cease to shake some part of your anatomy. As I leave, the Staff quiz me on how Dad is coping.

4pm: Dad visits you. Felt there were a couple of moments when you were in reality and talking normally. Actually stating to Dad that you want to remain in the 'real' world. Ate most of your supper. Hugged Dad. The staff hinted to him that you're receiving too many visitors. But overall Dad's encouraged.

6pm Jenifer and Peter visit. You react to their description of returning the boat to its moorings. Take Peter's glasses from him. You chat away about Theo. Your hands are deep in your pockets.

On Monday you will commence a new course of drugs – anti-depressants[1].

Sunday, June 13th

I decide to skip visiting today due to four lots of visitors going anyway. Dad phones at breakfast. You went to the dining room and peeled your own egg for breakfast, since when you've been sitting watching TV. Mary Evans visits you briefly. She's concerned about your right ear. I expect it is the latest part of your body to receive your undivided attention. There is probably physically nothing at odds with it.

Dad calls in to see you after lunch. Your latest obsession is with clocks and walls. But overall he finds you more lucid at intervals. You take his glasses and watch and show an interest in a list of official' visitors he is compiling for the staff, after a student nurse (Mark) got in minus an invite. You throw a cup to the ceiling, are noisy, keep your eyes open more and ask Dad for a drink.

Next Jenifer and Peter visit. They are impressed by the staff especially your key-worker Linda. She apparently wishes you had gone somewhere private when the physical check-ups were carried out. Peter thinks you have picked your right ear and your nose. Bruises are visible on your arms and legs. While they are there you hit your head accidentally on a drawer. You did say Peter's name. When he tries asking you why you hit your chest he gets no response.

The final visitor of the day is Helen Knott at 6pm.

Monday, June 14th

At 10.45 am I arrive at Park View and find you sitting up in a chair, fully dressed

---

[1] Amitriptyline, a tricyclic anti-depressant, was not prescribed until the 28th and then discontinued 2 days later. Ed.

with one of Dad's nightshirts over the top! Your hair has been washed and its fly away state is clearly irritating you. I suggest bringing in some of your hair combs, getting no response really. In fact for the majority of the time you are away in a world of your own. However, your eyes definitely remain more open. You mutter about me staying for a while at 1pm. Next, in quite impressive tones, you sing notes loudly that echo resoundingly up and down the Park View corridor. I think a 'Bastard' is aimed at me, as well as being called your 'Queen, Princess and bitch'.

New medication started today – anti-depressants. Last night you broke a windowpane by flinging a glass bottle. This was appreciated by all as a complete accident, 'One of those things', said Maggie. One nurse, back after a week off, commented on you looking fuller around the face. Today you ate your breakfast without help. The Unit is busy with a few new patients in.

You are still shaking your head and arms constantly and also taking your glasses on and off. In your room you read one of your birthday cards and it makes you cry. Then you push down on the basin taps and enjoy filling it up. In the afternoon Maggie suggested to Dad that we bring your watch in. Dr Ahmed sees you, failing to extract much clarity from you. You do comment on Dad's watercolour – liking it very much. The staff – Linda and Maggie – are determined to get you back to normal and working as before. Helen Knott spends 40 minutes with you in the evening.

Tuesday, June 15th

At 11am I arrive at Park View. I'm aware of workmen fixing the TV room window- panes as I park the car. My inkling is it's your doing. Sure enough Linda greets me with the full details. Last night the people smoking in the TV room, along with a hospital scene on the TV, agitated you. All the staff failed to contain your actions. The outcome – three broken windowpanes after a chair had been thrown at the window. The staff took you eventually to an intensive treatment room; injecting a drug[1] you were initially prescribed, to calm you down. What the staff call the 'hands on method'. This was all a bit frightening and horrendous sounding. I hate this happening to you.

Linda got you to move from the TV room to your own room when I arrived. I've given you an old watch of Dad's. You listen to it and place the watch face on your neck. Still shaking your head and hands continually. Sometimes you shout, quite often swear words, also singing the 'Wizard of Oz' merrily today. It's almost as if you're totally drunk and out of it. To prove that my presence has been noted you request that I pass you your Slush Puppy slippers. Next you wave and waft your arms at full length out of the open window. To me this symbolises a desire to be out there and free. Or perhaps you are gathering pure fresh air? Certainly the smokers in Park View annoy you. I stop you throwing a cup and pillows out onto the drive. There's so much anger in you. Physically you look fuller in the face and healthier, are steadier, more active and energetic.

---

[1] Probably 100mg Thioridazine, see appendix, Ed.

Dad visits you in the afternoon, experiences your usual odd moments of lucidity, also your singing and anger. Ian came to see Dad at home. He explained how you are behaving differently at Park View to how he had expected from your behaviour when still at home. Lynda visits in the evening and is convinced you're better again. You ate your supper; one slice of bread was thrown over your head.

Wednesday, June 16th

Dad visits you in the morning. I walk up to the school later to collect the car. In the afternoon I take socks and tracksuit bottoms to you. A new nurse, Jill, is with you. I find you in the dining room finishing your lunch. You are the last to finish but eventually all is eaten. Then you sing a bit, pause, look at me, 'Oh...............you're still here are you?' You willingly and easily walk with me to your room. Throughout my visit you are lucid; the best you've been for days. You chat to me, giving me instructions to put Dad's watercolour back up on your cupboard door. Interestingly, unlike Dad's old watch, which has gone missing, you know exactly where his watercolour is hiding. The ordering about continues, this time you want me to hinder entry into the room for anyone else by placing a chair in front of the door.

Do I comply? I decide to play along. You are certainly in a wicked mood today! You take your glasses on and off; strongly object to 'Hospital Property' being written on a towel and it's chucked over me. 'Get Stuffed!' You've apparently objected to Jill's bed-making skills, 'No OBE for that ' you told her, adding 'Other Bugger's Efforts'

Once again you object to my CCAT hockey team sweatshirt, it reminds you of your school days etc. I'm cross with myself for forgetting that it winds you up and quickly turn it inside out. The playful, childish and naughty acting-up continues. Is this what it is? The next source of entertainment is your handbag, which you find great amusement in calling your 'sin bin'. This name makes you smile. All the airmail stickers are placed neatly around Dad's watercolour. Again I'm not sure whether to stop this or not. Instinct tells me just to allow you to proceed and avoid antagonising you any more than I'm already doing by simply being there. The 'Anti-Xmas' badge that I gave you is found in your 'sin-bin'. You use it to rub away the hockey sticks on my sweatshirt. You make me move my chair so that I'm sitting opposite you. What a visit! Certainly you are into a new phase of behaviour. Overall I feel encouraged by some positive signs. Helen Knott visits in the evening.

Thursday, June 17th

At 8am Dad arrives and joins you for breakfast and at 2.45 the Andersons pop in to see you. Pauline visits at 6pm, phoning us afterwards to say she left you feeling, Pauline that is, happy and delighted at the progress you've made. You talked about Andy; about stars and when Pauline arrived you recognised her and even knew that it was her birthday. Prior to her arrival you had refused any supper. At 1.00am you phone home and I answer as Dad's away for the night. 'Can I speak to Dad? I hate it here and I want to come home. How long have I been here?' I am left with mixed feelings after that. Yes, obviously it's a good sign that you're up to phoning and questioning where you are, but equally it's hard to hear you so unhappy and basically knowing that I can do nothing. I feel useless and it's so frustrating. I sense you're missing Dad as well.

Friday, June 18th

I call Park View at 9am, checking that you're OK after phoning me in the early hours. A definite euphemism for a 'crap night' is the member of staff's answer, 'fairly okayish night, some sleep'. It turns out you weren't even in your own room for most of the night. I'm bloody sick of being fobbed off by the staff and not treated like an adult. I don't need protecting, stupid idiots. At least I believe them when they report that you've eaten breakfast.

Mid-morning Lynda visits and afterwards phones us to say she's delighted by your lucidity and rationality. You want to leave and come home. According to Lynda you have every right to, as you are an 'informal' patient. You are now refusing your medication, as you are entitled to, unless your calmness and relaxed behaviour ceases, when the staff have the weight of the law behind them to enforce you to take it. Equally, they could section you.

From 12.30 to 3.15 I visit you and you are warm and pleased to see me. But the lucidity Lynda witnessed seems to have drifted. Wilma – a name you shout hilariously and regularly, 'Flintstone's style' down the corridor – chats to me. She explains that Dr Ahmed does not want you to leave yet, even for a few hours, not until you are rational and lucid for a forty-eight hour stretch. Currently the periods of clarity are short before you drift. You are still confused and speaking nonsense.

Next Dr L came to see you in your room, Jill and I stay while he proposes a move to the 'open' Portia Ward. You imply that you're happy with this, but it is as though – similarly to when Dr B came to see you at home – you put up a huge front. Then as soon as Dr Whoever takes his leave, a period of unsettled and disturbed behaviour follows.

Nurse Linda is back after two days off. She sees that she's missed immense progress. She explains patiently to you that for your safety you must accept staying put. As soon as you are functioning fully you can go. Feelings of panic fill you. You clearly feel trapped in your room. You object to Linda's staff name badge. At 4pm Dad visits you.

10.45pm and you phone Dad saying you're unhappy and want to come home.

Saturday, June 19th

8am – Dad phones Park View to learn that you slept in your room until 1 am, then wouldn't go back and stayed in the lounge. Dad had breakfast with you. Thankfully you accept your medication again. This will slow down your mind helping you to sleep. He reads a letter from Jo to you.

The Hospital Chaplain visits you. At 12.30 Dad returns having stayed with you for lunch and at 3pm Jenifer and Peter call in to see you. Later I visit you, sitting with you and the other patients during supper. I find you very tired but lucid. In fact you virtually drop off at one point. You mention returning home this evening and ask how home is. What have I been doing? You are pleased that Jo is settled and happy in Worcester, but when is she returning? I learn that at night the noise levels, coming from staff or patients walking about and keys jangling, upset you and prevent you from switching off with consequent feelings of panic.

You're planning to visit the Chapel tomorrow and leave for home after that, but you do admit that you feel confused and very tired. This is hardly surprising after very little sleep last night. However, this continual requesting to leave Park View has to show an improvement, as does an interest in how home is. You compare a card sent by a friend to Dad's watercolour. At 7.30, when Dad visits once again, you're very tired – too many visitors today?

Sunday, June 20th

At 8am Dad phones for an update. You are actually still asleep and have had a good night, presumably knocked out by the medication once again, which you are continuing to take willingly. The staff will wake you for an 8.30 breakfast with Dad. Later on Mary Evans pops in to see you and then at 11.30 I arrive to spend some time with you, aware that earlier Dad had found you regressed and drifting. You were unaware of his presence, refusing to move to the dining room and slumping on your bedroom floor. You kept your eyes shut and were angry and unsettled. This was disappointing and difficult for Dad after a good visit yesterday. Just how much medication have they pumped into you? You are visibly struggling and confused after such long, deep, drug-induced sleep.

You look hot, probably aided by two grey woolly socks on one foot. You are certainly in your own busy world again, with the old physical actions in full swing, such as beating your chest and shaking your head. This is painful to witness after you've been so much better. Your suffering goes on. You slowly and gradually ate your lunch from a tray on your lap. At first you want me out of your sight, then in it. You give me a hug. Rapid mood swings are taking place. One minute you cry, the next you laugh. 'Too many voices' you complain. There is a frequent use of rhyming words. You strip your bed of all its bedding and won't allow me to remake it. You are getting rid of all the things with 'Hospital Property' written on them.

I escort you to the toilet, waiting outside for ages, listening to you singing away and growling angrily. 'She-She bears' you say. Your eyes are still shut often and when you open them it's as though you suddenly remember I'm there. Later Lynda visited and then Jenifer and Peter in the evening. For the first time you recall their previous visit. Peter suggests that it will be a zig-zagged recovery. He also thinks that we must stand up to your inaccurate mutterings. Today Christopher Richards, Julia, Chris Swinburn and Janey[1], all phoned.

Monday, June 21st
10.30am and Dad got me to drive him to Park View. I didn't go in but left him to see you. Meanwhile I took some photos of the place. Your night was okay, you had slept right through it. You were still angry and had been throwing pillows around. The visit ended with you shouting at Dad to stay longer, which obviously made him feel guilty at leaving after only a brief visit. I could hear your shouts from the grounds. That afternoon I visit you and find you watching Wimbledon. You eat raspberries, a gift from Cicely. At first you don't want any blackcurrant juice, mumbling that it is for the nighttime only. Although you are calmer you are still distinctly chatty and noisy and are still in a world of your own. You are lucid and rational for only a brief time. You are extremely aware of, and reacting to, other people chatting or conversing around you. A patient - Jill - calls you She-She and another patient Sue is disruptive and stares at me. She proceeds to ask you about your wedding and strokes your hair. She mumbles on about Christianity. Later you throw the TV controls out of the window and onto the road, having already moved your chair closer to the screen. You say that you want to go for a stroll, but after you have gone to the loo and got your shoes on in your own room, your mind has drifted away from the original plan of action.

Now you moan at yourself for brushing your hair too frequently. You object to a fly buzzing around, it totally irritates you. Today I hear one reference you make to someone about going home. Pauline visits you in the evening and later Jo phoned home for the latest. There was no one in so she called Park View to be told that you are up and okay.

Tuesday, June 22nd
We had phone calls from Jo, Peggy[2], Margaret H and Anne Oliver. Dad phones Park View and learns that your night was up and down. At 12.45pm I collect the car from Dad at the school. He's visited you earlier finding you difficult and unco-operative when he first arrived. You were sitting in the office and refusing to get up. You were also throwing pillows around. Linda and Dad take you to the interview room where Linda explains the grounds of your behaviour boundaries. Basically your earlier behaviour was not on. You calm down after that.

When I arrive it is to find you doing the crossword with Wilma, clearly quite lucid and rational. We go to your room where I give you the cardigan I'd brought in for you. You peer out of the window in a curious way, finally suggesting that

---

[1] Friend, sister-in-law, colleague and another sister-in-law, respectively, Ed.
[2] My mother's twin sister, Ed.

we go outside. On consulting Wilma, she and Barry (a member of staff) want me to take you into the back garden as it's enclosed. You immediately twig, 'I'm shut in', especially as I have to shut the garden gate as requested by Wilma. However you seem to relish the peace and tranquillity away from the inside of the building. You are keen that I should walk by you and not stalk you. I relaxed as I soon realised that a dash for freedom was not probable. You concentrated on getting your bearings, orientating yourself, as to the Unit's location and the surrounding view. You make connections with everything, for example the number plates of the cars in the car park remind you of different things. You decide the cat is enjoying home without you. Back inside I leave you peacefully and calmly reading and I have a good chat with Linda. You in turn had a good talk to her last week. I find you altogether much better today.

Helen Knott visits in the evening and Dad later to find you angry and noisy at first. After taking out your anger on him you calm down sufficiently to read to him. No doctor has seen you..............why?

Friday, June 25th
Lynda visits with Ben in the morning while D and I wait in the car. Lynda stays with you after Ben's said goodbye for the summer as he's off to the States. Dad cycles out to spend a few hours with you and I visit at 9pm, leaving once you are sleeping soundly. You are woken in the early hours by another patient.

Saturday, June 26th
Dad visits to discover that you've had a bad night.

Lynda visits in the afternoon and Jenifer and Peter pop in later. However you are too distant and disturbed for them to get anywhere. So they decide to leave fairly promptly. It is decided that you are not well enough to be visited by Jo who is back from Worcester. At 9pm Dad tries unsuccessfully to calm you down.

Sunday, June 27th
Dad saw you first thing. You are now lucid enough to see Jo for the first time and at 10.30am Jo and I find you waiting by the front door. You are very emotional and crying as you greet Jo with a hug. For the first 10-15 minutes you shake your head and are difficult. Suddenly you switch into lucidity: 'How was Worcester, Jo?' You take us for a walk to the chapel and once back we sit on the grass outside Park View. At midday Jenifer, Peter and Uncle Simon visit. Again you are very emotional at seeing a fresh visitor - in the form of Simon - but quickly pull yourself together and are lucid. Peter has half an hour with you saying how unacceptable some of your behaviour has been, indicating that you're close to being sectioned. You've already been in the Sin Bin due to hassling other patients and the staff and also for throwing things. Dad sees you in the evening.

Monday, June 28th

I visit to find you in a world of your own. We walk in the grounds for a while. I've a feeling that something's about to happen – harmful – so I feel nervous. Especially as you make a beeline for any dogs or crows on the large lawn, you throw sticks for the dogs. Later Dad visits to find you more lucid. Jo finds you switched on and calm when she visits. In the evening Pauline sees you and you make it clear that you wish to come home and when Dad visits again you are very lucid, enjoying reading and excited by your own intelligence.

Tuesday, June 29th

You had a fairly good night's sleep. This morning Dad didn't think you were very with it, not really wanting to talk much. You did go for a walk with him. Jo visited for a long time in the afternoon. During this, Dr L sees you. He really hits a nerve, asking you about your parents, consequently upsetting you greatly as well as Jo. He did say he feels that you can skip Portia Ward and come home. You've broken your glasses. You are lucid for the middle part of Jo's visit but unsettled for the rest.

When I arrive in the evening you are being difficult. So I put into practice a tactic that Peter suggested last Sunday. Because you were not making sense I told you I was going to leave. Sure enough you suddenly became rational and lucid. We walked around the grounds and I then left. I forget to retrieve my copper bangle that you'd borrowed from me.

Thursday, June 30th

Your sedation levels have been increased[1]. Apparently you are to have a brain scan next week. Meanwhile the staff have talked to Dad requesting that the immediate family visit only. However, Dad's persuaded them to allow Linda, Andy and Pauline to continue visiting. Also, another change, everyone must phone and check that visiting is okay first.

Sunday, July 4th

Peter feels happy that Park View have finally got the drugs right. Jenifer and Peter had good visits on Saturday and today. Apparently Bill Moore[2] had a breakdown, he's made a full recovery and merely takes Lithium daily. This will hopefully be the same for you.

Monday, July 5th

Finally it appears definite that you've had a 'psychotic breakdown'. This is when a person is not in touch with reality, 'mad'. A 'nervous breakdown' involves weepiness, bad nerves, an inability to cope, a loss of self-esteem and depression. Could this be a combination of both?

[1] This was a couple of doses of Chloral Hydrate 2g, given in the early mornings, Ed.
[2] My maternal uncle, Ed.

Tuesday, July 6th

You have been taken off tranquillisers. Yet another Park View experiment, another shot-in-the-dark, it involves putting you on a drug to slow down your thought process[1]. It is a one-off injection, thus increasing the speed at which the drug enters the blood. The brain scan will be on Friday.

Wednesday, July 7th

Last night was pretty awful for you as you had very little sleep. I pop in to see you first and of course you are very tired. You slur your words more, perhaps as a result of the drugs? You are not really able to say much. I wonder at the strength of this new drug as you climb into bed and fall asleep holding my hand. Is it necessary to turn you into a sleepy zombie? There is no doubt whatever that it is what they are trying now. I feel altogether uncomfortable with all this hapless experimenting. Clearly if you were not on the drugs then I expect you'd be manic and fairly disruptive. Dad laid down a challenge for the staff during his visit, presenting them with a first. He wishes to spend the night alone with you at Park View.

Thursday, July 8th

Now you are receiving drugs orally again to slow down your mind. Dr Ahmed is away this week, but somebody else saw you today. I visited you over lunchtime for a mixed hour and a half. I found your mind inaccessible to outsiders. Are you disturbed due to a busy morning with the doctor and psychologist? Frequently you go and pester the staff in the office. This is the place you're used to being on any ward normally. Your appetite has been poor over the last two days. I leave you sleeping. Dad learns from the hospital that you will be on full pay for six months, then on to half pay.

Friday July 9th

Jill and Wilma accompany you to the hospital this morning where you have a brain scan (CAT scan?) We learn that the immediate results (unofficial) indicate that you are fine with no problems physically. This confirms earlier physical examinations. Dad is the only visitor today, calling in after school. You eat your supper very slowly, as you are heavily drugged. You are asleep by 10pm.

Saturday, July 10th

After a bad night you are walking with Wilma when Dad phones. I visit in the afternoon and it's the best I've seen you for a while. By this I mean that you are lucid, calm and seemingly content. There is no noticeable anger today. You're not even flinching as doors slam. You are still weary and slow due to a combination of bad nights and drugs. Using charcoal, you sketch my hand as I sit opposite. During a visit from Jo later you become lucid after a shaky start.

---

[1] This must have been Droperidol 20mg – which was given in the early morning and again before midday, Ed.

Sunday, July 11th

After a reasonable night Dad is with you for a 9.30am service at the chapel. Afterwards you are depressed and weepy. You and Dad chat to Dave – a nurse? In the afternoon you sleep and have a late afternoon visit from the Andersons'. When I come in, I find you quite well apart from one wobbly period when you shake your head repeatedly. You are tired, but calm and fairly together. Sleeping in the afternoon has thrown your sense of time right off, so you keep thinking it's the morning. We went for a walk around the grounds. You are shaky on your feet resting occasionally on the roadside bollards, which you refer to as 'bollocks' rather sweetly. Later on Jo has a good visit too.

Monday, July 12th

This has been another good day for you during which your great sense of humour shines through. You are quite together, although still visibly weary and wobbly on your feet. You sketch my feet with my pointed black suede boots on. Wonderfully you maintain an accessible state all day long.

Tuesday, July 13th

I was away all day in Birmingham. Pauline visits at midday and tells you that she feels you're ready to be at home. 'You're more perceptive than many' you reply. Indeed, the fantastic news is that Dr Ahmed has agreed to let you come home for three hours on Wednesday evening. Will you want to return to Park View? Later in the afternoon Jo visits. You are very weepy at one point as a result of talking about past deaths and war. The sadness and weight of past events is emerging.   On your suggestion a nurse is present to support you both throughout. Dad visits in the late evening.

Wednesday, July 14th

On my arrival in the morning I discover that you have had a very good night. However, you were weepy once you woke up. You tell me you dealt with this yourself. Sleep invariably makes you slightly muddled and lost until you wake up fully. This is the effect of the drugs I imagine. You are lucid and rational. We walk the circuit and then you wake up D who's waiting in the car. We all sit in your room and do the Independent concise crossword. No problems for you in working out the majority of the clues. Before we leave I gently let you know that no-one will be popping in this afternoon, allowing you to rest prior to coming home tonight. 'I don't rely on visitors' is your response.   It is a lovely first visit home from 6 –9pm. You are so calm, relaxed and humorous.

Thursday, July 15th

Dad had phoned and discovered that you'd had a good night and were still sleeping. When I arrive I'm pleased to find that you are still as well as you were last night. We walk around the grounds. You do not dilly-dally as you want to be back in case Ahmed arrives. Obviously we are all hoping home visits will become the norm. You win a game of chess before I leave. As you see me off, the workmen are back again, replacing glass in the men's ward, clearly they recognise you and appear amazed at the progress that you've made. Andy visits in the evening. Dr Ahmed has reduced your medication and sure enough he's allowing you home tomorrow evening and then all day Saturday and Sunday. He will review the situation at the end of the week and it's looking highly likely that you'll come home for good then. The news gets better! Dad is with you from 8pm.

Friday, July 16th
Jo's birthday and we have a birthday tea. You have a good visit home and return to Park View for the night, likewise on Saturday, and on Sunday you are home for the whole day. During this time there is an emergency admission to the ward and your room is occupied, so you are home PERMANENTLY. The staff have decided that you only need to go there for a doctor's appointment on the following Thursday.

Wednesday, August 18th
After being based at home for exactly a month, you visit the Day Centre and the doctor there re-admitted you. He required only one look at you and is in awe as to how Dad and Jo coped. So you are back at Park View.

Saturday, August 21st
Due to one, or maybe more, of the various drugs you've been taking you now have a very low blood pressure. This makes you shaky on your feet. I return from a month away, to find you thinner and with a new short hairstyle. Is this really my Mum?
There is quite a transformation in the way you look. Overall it makes you look younger.

Sunday, August 22nd
When I visit you at Park View you are overwhelmingly sad, discussing suicide with Linda and me.

Thursday, August 26th
Today you start taking Lithium. You've had a good walk, talk and a few tears with Vicky, discussing work problems. You are having a stint in the open Portia ward prior to returning home, this time for good. The move from Park View was instigated due to you maintaining constant lucidity and rationality. You appear far more balanced and at peace with things. While at Portia the biggest challenge is time and filling it. Unfilled stretches of time pose a daunting challenge to you, really dragging and causing boredom. So you willingly go to

Keep Fit, Occupational Therapy and Art classes on and off. A flow of visitors helps pass the time. They normally accompany you on walks around the grounds. Jenifer buys you knitting needles, wool and a pattern or two to help you take up another occupation. All of the activities give you something to focus on and help build up your confidence slowly. Nightmares are common for you while at Portia.

All the hospital meals are consumed conscientiously by you, disciplined by now over the need for food and being very good at looking out for your own dietary needs. We supplement dull, unimaginative food by bringing in fruit. Often you get up for breakfast and return to bed for more sleep afterwards, prior to your first activity – normally at 10am.

Wednesday, October 29th, the day you leave Portia and the hospital for good. Back at home you are concerned about time and filling your days: you are not ready to be left alone.

Thursday, October 30th
I join you at one of your sessions with a clinical psychologist.

9. JO'S DIARY

2nd June 1993

Over the space of a week my Mum, my invincible, strong Mum, has had a nervous breakdown (though I use this term hesitantly). First she wasn't sleeping at all and now she can't sleep or eat, is talking all the time and has to have someone with her constantly.

The doctor said it was 'chronic stress' at first. Mum has been seen by her psychotherapist, Pat and by a psychiatrist. Tonight Rachel telephoned to say mum has been admitted to Park View overnight. Tomorrow she is going to a special hospital in Wells.

What the hell am I doing sitting here, writing this when my sister and Dad are at home going through a nightmare and my Mum is losing it totally? My God it's funny, it really is a sick joke.

Pops and Rachel hired a nurse so they could have a night's sleep - Mum called the nurse 'Shaggy Baggy'. Apparently she has referred to me as 'Princess Jo'. I'm so frightened. My poor Dad has lost his wife. Please God bring her back soon - I'll always appreciate her if you do. I love my family so much. Dad and Rachel couldn't even give Mum a bath.

3rd June 1993

Mum is 51 on Sunday and I don't think she will even know what is going on inside her head. My poor Mum. I can't imagine what they have all been through/are going through at home.

4th June 1993

Apparently Park View is a ward at the psychiatric hospital near Taunton. Mum is still there, she won't be moved to Wells until she is much more in control. I believe Pops said Park View is an intensive, secure ward. I feel guilty and useless being here. The good news is Mum recognises Dad and Rachel- she does 'know' them.

6th June 1993

Happy Birthday Mum. I haven't rung home yet today. I feel as if I'm in a trance.

Mum is lying in a hospital room and I have exams in ten days. My uncle seems to think Mum will be in hospital for a number of weeks. My last exam is 23rd June - then I can go home and free Rachel and D (R's friend) to go to Birmingham. Ben is off to America on the 25th. Basically I can take over where Rachel has left off, supporting Pops and visiting Mum. It is likely she will still be in hospital when I get home. I'm finding it difficult to concentrate on anything at the moment - my brain is so fuzzy. I just need to snap myself out of this haze and concentrate on revising. Pops is back to work tomorrow but he's going to take long lunch-breaks to rest. Lynda spent some time with him yesterday and massaged his feet to help soothe his anxieties and feelings of loss.

8th June 1993

Just telephoned Pops. Mum's latest trick is climbing under her bed so they have put her mattress on the floor. Dad said she was extremely amorous today (!). Mum ate some soup which is good. Tomorrow she is having X-rays to check nothing is wrong physically.

12th June 1993

Dear Mum, please come back soon, I miss you very much and basically you're someone I respect a lot. I feel as if someone has ripped the rug from under my feet but I'm still managing to balance.

Dear Ben, you've let me down. Why don't you ring or write and ask me how I am. Why aren't you at home now. What if you go to America and Mum asks for her son?

Dear Dad, I wish you'd speak more quickly when I ring you from a pay-phone. I wish you still had your wife, at home, lying beside you in bed now. I wish she'd answer the phone in her clear, confident voice and call me 'darling'.

Dear God, sort it out, this has gone far enough. Oh, and please can I pass my exams?

Dear Mum, come back, come back, come back. I love you. I know we have our problems but we get on all right, it's just we're too similar sometimes. Or maybe that's not it at all. Bollocks.

Dear Dad, I love you but you annoy the hell out of me. I hope my kids treat me better than I've treated you.

14th June 1993

Dear Jo, get out of your own head and heart and cope. Be strong, cry on your own and gain a sense of perspective. Things can probably only improve. Have some maturity and concentrate on the good things about life. P.S. and stop talking to yourself.

Rachel and Jo

19th June 1993

Mum is having long periods of being lucid and rational. She telephoned home in the early hours of Friday morning and told Rachel she hates it in Tone Vale and wants to come home. Mum also asked how long she'd been in hospital for. Dad was actually away at a conference, Mum was wanting to speak to him, but Rachel reminded her of where he was and she took it OK. For a couple of days last week Mum refused to take her medication and threatened to discharge herself.

I telephoned home tonight and spoke to Dad and Rachel and the conversation left me feeling rather uneasy. They both sounded rather strained. They just said that a lot of visitors had taken their toll on Mum and she'd had enough by the end of the day. Rachel said she asked after me too.

24th June 1993

Mum is very up and down. She is still having periods when she is quite in control but the downs are quite distressing. Dad has been tearful on the phone lately and I think (I mean, God, understandably) he is finding it very difficult. Ben is home and will be spending most of today with Mum. The reunion (Pops took Ben to see Mum last night) was emotional, but Mum seemed to have quite a clear grasp of the fact that Ben is off to the States. Mum has taken to reading poetry (sometimes out loud to visitors), Dad asked her if she fancied some Shakespeare and she asked for 'The Merchant of Venice'. Mad intellectuals, I don't know!

I am anxious to get home but am adjusting to the idea of home-life, as it is now, with some trepidation. I must be calm and relaxed when I see Mum or else I'll make her more uptight.

27th June 1993

I've been reunited with my darling Mum. I was shocked and disappointed with Park View. We were let into the main doors and Mum was just standing there and she looked disturbed and alone. We just hugged each other and cried. I think Mum sobbed that she was pleased to see me and I kept saying 'hello Mum' (profoundly original of me). Rachel and I walked Mum back to her room. She ranted and raved and wasn't in control and pulled at her hair, was very unsettled and just babbling nonsense. Then somehow composed herself, looked at me, and said 'So how's Worcester'? And for the rest of the visit she was almost her old self - asking questions, remembering things, collected. She walked with us to the Chapel and then we sat outside for a bit and talked.

As is fairly typical of me, I imagined Park View as much nicer/more glamorous than it actually is. Mum's room is so bare and cold. We established she'd like one of the duvets from the the-parental-bed-supreme so Dad has just gone to visit armed with a friendly, familiar home duvet, plus cherries, raspberries and a French stick.

I mustn't be frightened. I just find it incredible that Mum is in this situation at the moment. I always worried that Mum or Dad would be involved in a car crash or something, mental illness wasn't an option that ever crossed my mind.

Mum's eyes looked dead. Rachel tells me that's the drugs she's taking. She looked very pale (tired, inside most of the time). Her hair is in a fairly short bob, all the same length and she let me pull some of it away from her face with a comb. I noticed she is becoming greyer; she complained about it, but it's really pretty grey.

29th June 1993

I spent two hours with Mum today and it was quite painful. She wasn't in control and while the doctor was talking to her, he opened up some really, really sore wounds, and Mum was very distressed and upset. It looks as if it's going to be 'Park View' or home in stages i.e. first just for a night.

Mum told the doctor she feels extremely sad. I can't bear to see her like this, I want to put a brave face on things but I always cry at some point. Mum is so disturbed, she is suffering so much, what can I do to be a positive, definite help to her? I hope she can come home soon.

19th July 1993

A lovely long weekend off heralded many wonderful moments. At this moment Dad lies sleeping in his bed with his wife. Mum is home, in her own beautiful house with her family. On Thursday afternoon Mum will hopefully be officially discharged. She continues to be prescribed drugs.

2nd August 1993

Writing this exactly two weeks after Mum's escape/release/ departure from hospital. After the euphoria of the first few days of having Mum at home full-time, Dad and I realised that she was not coping as well as we first thought. She is here in body but her old spirit is definitely not with us. She and Dad are inseparable, Mum feels most at ease when she is with Dad, but obviously this puts quite a strain on Dad as he needs breaks too. It's not just the care, his emotions are inextricably linked to Mum and I really don't know how he is coping inside.

Predictably I am taking predominantly a domestic role in all this, making sure the kitchen is tidy, washing-up and cooking a main meal for them each day. Also I'm working and welcoming any opportunity of a social life.

I feel trapped by the situation, but I also feel I'm not doing enough - particularly on the emotional-support side. I still can't really comprehend how this could have happened to my Mum. She is sad, weak and vulnerable. Sometimes her eyes are dead. I don't know if it's a question of 'fighting' when one is dealing with mental illness, but I don't feel Mum is fighting at all. Maybe she is just not able to at the moment.

Mum is taking three-quarters of the drugs she was being prescribed in hospital, which is a hell of a lot. My fear is that if they are reduced she will become manic and incoherent again. What my mother is going through has really knocked my confidence in life and the world at large. Not one of us can really rely on our own sanity. You couldn't have met a more level-headed, unflappable, strong woman than Sheila Harvey. And now I sit by her bed while she sleeps in case she wakes up and panics because she is alone.

Meanwhile Ben has fun in America and Rachel suns herself in France. Bitter words but read on as I defend my siblings in the same breath. If I were in Ben's situation, I would probably have done exactly the same thing and gone out to join my partner as planned. But I'm still angry with him. Mum dotes on him and she will be so thrilled to see him and you won't hear a word of criticism from either of the parents against Ben for abandoning ship in their hour of need. Rachel has definitely earned a break as she has supported M&D through the earliest and perhaps most frightening stage of Mum's illness.

3rd August 1993

Some positive feedback! I'm getting some appreciation and approval from M&D. Mum actually said I'm very good at making her relax when she has one of her panic attacks in the form of shaking legs and arms. I can calm her down quite quickly, but I was so touched when she commented on it.

They both saw the psychiatrist today. He has reduced Mum's medication - I think by a third - and if she remains steady, it can be reduced again this Sunday. Please let her be OK. I think deep down Mum is really frightened she'll never be completely herself again. I really sense she is full of fear and self-doubt. I'm working a lot this week and I feel guilty because it means M&D are on their own, but they have coped so far.

18th August 1993

A day full of relief and great sadness. Poor Mum has been having a terrible time and is back in Park View. She was at home with us for almost a month and was needing constant care and was very unsettled. I just wish I could trust the Park View set-up more. It was heartbreaking to visit Mum there again. Because she had been sprung on them, Mum was in a bare room with just her bed in it. When Dad and I walked in she was lying on the bed in her top and knickers and was in a dreadful state; heavily drugged but still very agitated. It seems to me that as soon as a patient is difficult they pump them full of more drugs.

Mum's eyes were completely dead and her face even looked swollen. If she'd been at home today she wouldn't have had to go through that. This feels like a documentary horror story.

My Mum is desperately ill and it just feels as if no one knows how to make her better. Please someone make Mum well again, she has everything to live for. Pops is tearful but being very brave and finding comfort with his family, friends and religious beliefs. Rachel and D are home tomorrow night (hurray!) and willing to be based here for a while. This means Dad and I are able to go away for a few days soon.

23rd October 1993

At home things are encouraging. I heard yesterday from Rachel that Mum is home at the moment for a long weekend, and may be discharged on Thursday 28th October. I am trying not to feel too excited, but the most significant thing is Rachel tells me Mum's attitude has changed. She is now determined to get better. This fills me with hope because the last time I saw Mum she expressed her fear of never being 'normal' again and that she might die, that she had nothing to live for.

Now it seems she really is strong enough to fight. You can do it Mum. It's really impossible to 'help' when I am 100 miles away. I write and ring every week but obviously it just isn't the same as being there. I am so grateful to Rachel, she has done so much and seems content to stay at home for M&D at the moment.

Not sure on date of this entry -

On Monday Mum had her big meeting with her boss, to establish her future in the hospital. I still can't quite believe it, but basically she hasn't got one. She has to take early retirement. It's such a kick in the teeth for her, it's so undignified. It isn't what Mum deserves. It's not Mum's fault that she had a nervous breakdown. She has recovered well. I can't believe they weren't even prepared to offer her a nurse's post. I hate them. How can they treat Mum like that? For longer than my 24 years Mum has worked hard and well as a nurse. Then, in a matter of minutes, it all comes to an abrupt, ungrateful end. Hospital fucking management. A massive part of Mum's life has just been taken away. The routine that structured her existence. She is only 52 and doesn't want to retire.

A later date

Mum is appealing about her enforced early retirement. I worry that this process may bring her more pain, but it has to be done, to show the hospital Mum is serious about what she feels her abilities are.

JO'S RETROSPECTIVE THOUGHTS

(AT LEAST TWO YEARS LATER)

My New Perspective

The experience of watching someone so close to me temporarily break down and lose control, has taught me to appreciate life at a much more basic level. Now I am grateful that those I love are well and sane.

It was also a poignant lesson in taking nothing for granted in this life. Up until Mum's breakdown my imaginative processes in terms of 'disasters that could befall my parents' had been somewhat limited. In fact my sole worry was that they would meet with a gruesome car accident. Consequently Mum's rather dramatic mental illness came as a rude shock!!

Funny Moments

On one occasion when I was visiting Mum at Park View I experienced an interesting role-reversal. Mum was being quite loopy and decided to take refuge behind the arm-chair by her bed. She squeezed herself into this small space and sat there muttering. I found myself sitting on the bed and calmly saying, 'Come out from behind the chair please Mum, you will hurt yourself'. I reasoned with her in the same patient way I would reason with a naughty child. It struck me at that moment that we had swapped roles - I was now the parent and she was the vulnerable child.

Mum has a wicked streak and this certainly came through when she had the ultimate excuse to 'be bad'. During the month she was at home (somewhat prematurely), Pops and I had set up a game of croquet. I think we were struggling to keep her focused at this point. Mid-game, a member of the local clergy strolled into the garden and greeted us:- 'Oh this is very English Country Gardens, isn't it?' Eventually she turned to Mum and asked earnestly 'So how are you Sheila?' Mum's reply as she walloped a croquet ball into the distance was: 'Actually I'm sick to death of these bloody, bloody balls.' Our visitor looked a little stunned and I whispered 'nice one Mum'. We then smirked at each other gleefully - Mum knowing perfectly well that she had been rude. Personally I found it very refreshing - I can't stomach patronising do-gooders.

Attitudes

I think Pops should win an award for his open approach to his wife's illness. He never saw any reason to hide what was happening from the wider community. He was honest with everyone and didn't care who knew. As far as he was concerned, his wife was ill and needed help and support as did the family. My sister and I joked rather nervously, that we were half expecting to see the headline ' Local Head Teacher's Wife Goes Bonkers'..and he tells all in the local paper.

Sweet Moments

Clearly it was my parents' great love for each other that kept them going. But Pops also had 'the two Gs', in other words 'God' and 'Golf'. I remember Pops coming to talk to me looking exhausted and miserable. 'Jo, I think I just need three hours on the golf course and I'll feel much better'. Needless to say this was arranged.

A lot of the time Mum was particularly affectionate and sweet - partly due to regressive behaviour. One evening we washed up together and Mum sang to me 'Doey, I love my Doey'. Then we giggled together.

Exploitative Moments

Having to keep Mum occupied and on the go was obviously a sign that she wasn't ready to be at home for that first month. However, it was necessary to help Mum feel at ease. We were discussing what we could do next and I was feeling particularly like just sitting and being quiet. I spotted my pile of ironing and said very evenly- 'Well you could do my ironing Mum'. About half an hour's worth of ironing later and Mum wasn't so sure about this idea: 'You don't really bother with ironing your pyjamas do you Jo?' We laughed - it was a wonderful moment. Mum was well enough to be bored. There was hope for a more 'normal' existence.

Advice

One thing that certainly should have been established by now about mental illness is that it has to be accompanied by feelings of helplessness, loss, confusion and anxiety - particularly in terms of recovery hopes.

Why then did several intelligent, professional and close friends of my family see fit to tell my sister and myself that – 'these sorts of things tend to run in the family you know'. I will regret forever not replying:- 'I see, so you mean that we have a chance of being mentally ill in the future. Great, how comforting. You know I am feeling upset and worried about my Mum but now that you've told me that, suddenly I feel much better'. No apologies for heavy sarcasm here.

Present Moments

I will always have empathy and concern for those whose lives are being affected by mental illness. The Press is guilty of labelling the mentally ill in an abusive, negative manner and hyping-up the fact that they could be a danger to society.

It should be remembered that in our most general form, we - society - are the cause of mental illness and we should check our own attitudes and behaviour before we condemn. I am extremely proud of my Mum; not least because she gave lithium the boot a long time ago.

Doctors take note: drugs may be the answer for a while but the goal should be no medication. It appears to be the case that the doctors aim to get the drugs right so that patients will get on with their lives and leave the medical profession alone. This attitude doesn't allow for people who don't want to rot away on drugs, but instead take responsibility for their own health and mental well-being. My Mum is doing very nicely without medication thank you very much.

Mermaids with Ben   *Jo*   *Rachel*

Sheila and Ben

10. BEN'S 'EPISODES APART'

Mum would go to Bath. I knew the routine. In the morning, she'd catch the inter-city from Taunton to Bristol Temple Meads, before changing onto a local train for the shorter leg of the trip. In the evening the journey was reversed and often she'd phone from either Bath or Bristol to tell us that she was on her way home. Occasionally, after the call, we would stand just outside our garden fence – from where we could see the tracks cross a bridge – and wave as her train sped past, bringing her home.

Imagining her making the journey was easy enough – I'd done it a few times myself. Bath was where we might go for a family excursion, either to shop (Hamley's, the toy store, was there), or to see Phil Savery, a family friend who lived in an 'old curiosity shop', close to the Abbey. But why did Mum go? My sisters and I weren't sure. The reason for her pilgrimages was as mysterious as their spacing, which, like irregular heart beats, were sometimes far apart and at other times clumped together. Then they would stop altogether for long periods....only to resume again. The official, parentally sanctioned, reason for the trips was, I think, 'work'. But, although it often involved strange hours, late nights and early mornings, nursing had a thoroughly predictable rhythm to it, a rhythm foreign to these episodes apart. So I began to suspect that there was something other than work taking place in the city of the soothing waters.

Eventually, perhaps it was during the later 'eighties, Mum and Dad's story changed and we were given a different explanation for the trips – one that began to unpack the silent anxiety accompanying them. The new word was 'therapy' and this was supplemented by the therapist's name. It was always just 'Pat', a single, androgynous syllable standing alone, a noun that was also a verb. Things happened between Mum and Pat, although I didn't quite know what. I understood a little about therapy – a few of my parents' friends were even therapists – but my mind was left to fill the considerable blanks. I pictured a darkened room, conversations, perhaps even tears and anger. Whatever Pat did, she was clearly a necessary part of the process, whether as confidant or adversary. Suspecting the worst, I tended to favour the latter option and imagined her as Mum's sparring partner in the Spa town, but clearly the better boxer. And on her return from these bouts, it was now understood that Mum might be bruised and should be handled with care.

The Double portrait - my own image -
an attempt at self-reflection. Jeremy concentrates on his own art

Had Mum not changed trains at Bristol Temple Meads on her irregular trips to Bath, she might have ended up in Birmingham, and it was here I went to university in 1991. I mention this because it was in Birmingham that I last saw Mum before her 'breakdown'. It was May 16th, 1993, my 21st birthday and to commemorate the event a group of family friends shared a meal at a favourite Indian restaurant, the Sundarbon in Selly Oak. After we'd eaten and downed the obligatory champagne, it was time for me to open cards and presents. Among these was a flat, oblong package from my parents and, having torn the wrapping off, I saw that the present was my parents – a water colour of them, framed in glass. A bespectacled, middle-aged couple, standing side by side, represented from the chest up. Dad to the right, Mum to the left. My parents and yet not my parents. For whereas Dad was Dad, Mum was barely recognisable: or, I should say, barely recognisable to me. The figure on the right, I knew, was a self-portrait; Mum was the artist. So presumably she had thought that this shrunken person with the frightened eyes somehow corresponded to what she had seen in the mirror. Feeling somewhat embarrassed, I mumbled my insincere thanks and, on returning to my bedroom, placed the picture in a drawer. Face down.

Megan, who's now my wife but was then my long distance girlfriend, was not in Britain for my twenty-first: but, quite coincidentally, our emails of the time touched upon a subject that was soon to have more immediate relevance.

May 14,1993 (Megan to Ben; Santa Barbara, California, to Birmingham England)

Last night after the play I headed off to Carrow's, a 24 hr diner, to study at the counter. Classic setting. I ordered a cup of coffee, which in classic diner style was constantly refilled. Two older men sat to my right. Obviously regulars, like nightly regulars, both chain smoking (cough cough). Then an elderly man sat to my left, also smoking the strongest of cigarettes. What's a good British phrase for crazy? I know the 'a few sandwiches short of a picnic' one. The guy to my right said later, 'I think his tank was only half full'. You get the point. From the moment he sat down, he wouldn't stop talking. He talked first to the waitress, who avoided our end of the bar like the plague afterwards (so much for refillable coffee) and then to me before I realised that all I needed to do was just keep on reading (well, at least try). It made little difference to him, he just kept on talking, bursting into laughter, having conversations with the empty air in front of him and empty seat to his left. At one point he addressed me, saying 'hey, did you see that?' and pointing upwards. I never figured out what it was that he thought he was seeing or if he really expected me to see it. Said something about his doctor (I assumed psychiatrist) saying he needn't worry about the flying objects he saw, they wouldn't hurt him. It was up to him to make them go away.........my oh my! An evening of insanity.

May 17,1993 (Ben to Megan; Birmingham, England to Santa Barbara,

California)
   Phrases for insanity?
   Can short of a six-pack.
   The lights are on but nobody's at home (my favourite).
   The elevator doesn't go right to the top.
   What is this human need to turn insanity into a humorous subject?
Deeply revealing no doubt. Dr Johnson called madness 'the dangerous
prevalence of the imagination' - not the imagination in our sense of the
word, but when images in your head replace images derived from the outside
world. Now you know!

Like these conversations, Mum's drawing, which I now think of as an intimation of insanity, did nothing to prepare me for the shock of what happened just a few weeks later. Dad and Rachel had been the first to break the news to me and there was something tragic-comic about what I was hearing in Rachel's phone reports, something surreal about imagining one's own mother behaving like this. This can't be happening; this is not Mum. This is happening; this is Mum. Throughout her 'breakdown', the latter responses didn't replace the first, but shared the same contradictory space.

29 May, 1993(Ben to Megan)
And now I have some interesting news for you. Interesting but worrying. It's
my Mum. I phoned up last night to chat to the parents before they flew to
France and Dad answered. He had his 'everything's under control, honest'
voice on - terse and forced, so I knew something was up. Well, it seems as if
Mum's had some sort of mental and physical breakdown (I hate the
associations that word has). It's been difficult to extract anything more out
of Dad or Rachel (who phoned me back later) than that. She's been unable
to sleep because she's been thinking compulsively - unable to let her mind
stop racing. But she continued working full-time and, no doubt, continued
her doctorate. It all got too much and they pulled the plug on the holiday so
they could just have a week of peace together. Rachel says she was talking a
lot about her childhood and family so I guess it has its roots there - she's
seeing Pat (her old psychotherapist whom she saw regularly a few years
back) today. What drama. Both Dad and Rachel were telling me that it's
nothing too bad and that I shouldn't worry inordinately, but that's easier
said than done. And they couldn't disguise the anxiety in their voices.

31 May (Ben to Megan)
Chatted to Jo on the phone yesterday - she had just found out about Mum
and was basically extracting all I knew out of me. She was obviously upset,
but I hoped I helped her. Otherwise the news is the same on that front - no
news is good news, right?

3 June (Ben to Megan)
I feel emotionally drained at the moment. It's all been too much. Got back from the cinema last night to find a message on our notice board saying 'Ben, ring home for an update on your mother ASAP. Well, it was after midnight, so I rang this morning instead. And......Mum is now in hospital, being looked after by professionals, full-time. By the sounds of it, drugs are having no effect - they can't help her to sleep. By the sounds of it, she's not talking coherently. Anyhow, Anyhow, Anyhow after three or four experts discussed the situation for a couple of hours (including my Uncle Peter, who's got back from China and, as psychiatrist, wanted to see Mum for himself) they decided she'd be best in hospital, where they could sedate her and give her some rest. Once she's calmed down a little she may be moved to a ward in Wells (a little, picturesque city in Somerset) which has beds for people in Mum's situation.

I spoke to Dad on the phone - he sounded okay - relatively relaxed and optimistic considering everything. I've told him that I'll try and come down to see them all before California, an idea he liked. So that's the situation. It all seems so difficult to assimilate at the moment - no doubt seeing her for myself will be the only thing that can put it all into some sort of context. I also worry about how Jo will take the news, because I think she's likely to be a lot more upset than me.

4 June (Ben to Megan)
I did type, so what's happening? Maybe it was just slower than usual. Anyhow, I had important news to tell you yesterday. I'll summarise: Mum's in hospital. Short and to the point, but says it all. Too much to handle at home and - without the right equipment - it was doing no good to her body. But now she can be sedated up to the eyeballs, and her brain can be forced to stop. Great, right? I keep remembering the last Mum I saw, the Mum who attended my 21st celebrations. She was fit, looking great, alert and had her usual sense of humour. Will the Mum I see when I return to Taunton be anything like this?? I don't know. A letter from Jo came this morning sharing her distress.

June 7 (Ben to Megan)
It was my Mum's birthday yesterday. I sent her a card with a picture by Klee on it - a kind of fitting image - a fragmented head and shoulders broken up into wonderful colours and harmonies. The whole thing is hopeful though, just because it's so beautiful. Maybe I have to get used to this; Mum is just going to be beautiful in different ways.........I can't hope for the Mum whom I know to be there when I visit her, so I'm going to have to start again from scratch to some extent.

I go to London this Friday…I might go up on the Thursday night in order to see Jemma and Peter - get the expert's opinion on Mum. Apparently, he's wondering whether it may have some sort of physiological root - asking for appropriate tests to be done…I'll go home on the 23rd of this month - I'll have a day to see Mum and be with the rest of the family, and then Rachel can drive me up to Gatwick on the 25th.

Putting up barriers? Maybe…what else can I do? I have no real insight into the situation and am feeling too rational to get totally upset about something that I can't see and is beyond my control. Only when I write about it, or think solely about it, do I cry. I suppose the façade is in place as far as those around me can tell. Emma, Marion, Caroline et al - they all know, I'm telling them what's happening, but I'm refusing to get upset in their presence and it doesn't seem to be too much of a struggle. My lights are on, but nobody's home.

Our conversation about terms for madness now seems more than a little ironic. What I want to know is how I will react when I see Mum? I have no idea. I am unprepared. Maybe she won't recognise me. Maybe I won't recognise her. Anyhow, I rationalise things nicely: don't feel guilty about going to America, it's what Mum would have wanted….

Note the past tense.

Is Mum dead?

Spoke to Jo earlier in the day - she went to see family over the weekend: Aunt Sheila and Uncle Patrick plus sprog Peter. Obviously seeking sanctuary in relatives and a family unit. Jo is trying to revise for her exams but can't stop thinking about Mum. Consequence: she's getting no work done…………..We skirt the issue…Am I allowed to be happy?…because I think I am.

Human emotions are perverse.

Maybe it's the thought of escaping that keeps me going.

It was America that offered me my escape route. I had long been planning to spend my three month summer holiday with Megan on the West Coast. But before I crossed the Atlantic, I returned to Taunton for a weekend with the family, taking an afternoon train from Birmingham on a pleasant Friday in late June. Because I would shortly be seeing Megan in person, there was no need to write an email to her and consequently I have no written record of this visit, just more distant memories. That evening Dad and I went to the Reimers' for supper, and I can remember eating baked Alaska in their garden. At some point, Pauline took me aside and, putting on her social worker's hat, gently warned me to expect the worse with Mum. Despite (or because of) her good intentions, this distinctly irritated me. For I was prepared for the worst, for what could not be happening.

Starting the following morning, I made several short visits that weekend to the institution where Mum was staying. Rachel would drive me there through the pretty Somerset countryside to the building, which, at least on the outside, seemed similarly idyllic and pastoral. The large lawns, well-tended shrubs and backdrop of hills created a strong contrast to the austere, functional interior of the Victorian building. My memories of my time with Mum conform to no coherent pattern. There was her physical state – her palms rubbed raw, her hair dishevelled, her tendency to collapse unexpectedly. And there was the way she would make astute and funny comments about her doctors and fellow patients – mealtimes seemed to be particularly fertile in this respect. One morning I went on a walk with her around the grounds and she delighted in finding a huge, plate-sized mushroom growing on the lawn. She proceeded to peel off the fungus's outer layer of skin, and took a few bites from it. My initial concern (was this really just a harmless mushroom?) was gradually replaced by a feeling of relief and recognition, since this was just the sort of thing that Mum might normally have done. Less familiar, though, was her response to the thunderous, low flying planes that would intermittently swoop overhead. She would interweave these with other elements of her surroundings and produce elaborate scenarios of wartime persecution: mustard gas and trenches, bombing and bodies.

Mum would usually quote freely and fluently from certain poems she had memorised. One in particular sticks in my mind: Gerard Manley Hopkins' 'No worst, there is none', which seems to voice the feelings of someone suffering tremendous mental and spiritual anguish and imploring for aid:

> *No worst, there is none. Pitched past pitch of grief,*
> *More pangs will, schooled at forepangs, wilder wring.*
> *Comforter, where, where is your comforting?*
> *Mary, mother of us, where is your relief?*

So how much comfort, how much relief, did the son offer the mother? Not a great deal, I suspect and certainly not as much as the other members of my immediate family, who were often helping her on a day-to-day basis. Instead, I was having my own episodes apart, episodes studying at University, travelling in America, where my only contact was by mail and an occasional phone call. And by the time I returned to Britain in the early autumn, the worst of Mum's illness was over. She was spending more and more time at home, less and less away and my next letters to Megan talked about her breakdown as something of the past.

October 19 (Ben to Megan)
Have been back in Birmingham for just a day, and am still mulling over the
things Mum said. She said a lot about what it was like to be 'mad' - entering
a world where the normal laws mean nothing and the mind invents its own
truth. She went through a phase when she thought she was Florence
Nightingale, nursing in the Crimean War. One of her fears was that I'd be
arrested through customs with drugs in my guitar case. You turned up in the
guise of an American nurse she used to know (and like!). She also spent time
looking for the local vicar in the grass! Sometimes, something someone says
(that's a strange sequence of words) will bring a memory of the breakdown
back to her. For instance, I mentioned 'shit', and then looked at Mum and
she was in tears. She'd had this vision of a cathedral covered in faeces
apparently[1].

November 1 (Ben to Megan)
I was asleep this morning when my Mum rang. She went on about what was
going to happen to Lenin's brain...most peculiar. Something she'd read in the
paper and thought I should know. I think it was just an excuse to talk to me
- a novelty considering she used to detest the phone. But this time there was
no urgency in her voice, no hurry, no hurry. She's living at home. She sounds
STRONG, her voice more confident, her mind more concentrated. Life has
pleasure in it now, she says.

---

[1] I'm not sure on this one. I must have been borrowing/confused with/directly referring to Jung's vision of a giant turd falling on Basle Cathedral, Ed.

11. SHEILA'S EARLY LIFE –
AN ELDER SISTER'S PERSPECTIVE.

This account was written for the psychiatric team in 1993.

Mother – Rosemary - lively doctor's daughter, qualified pharmacist. Calm, accepting of fate and good at coping. Slightly in the shadow of David our father, but shared and kept up with my father's interests and was probably keener on sport and better than him at it. One of five children and a non-identical twin. She died in 1989, all her sibs are still living.

Father – David - son of an Indian Army Officer who committed suicide when D was two, although he was never told this. Only sister Mollie - a gifted artist, was killed in a car crash on her honeymoon. Strong evangelical Christian background and belief until interned by the Japanese. Popular and a raconteur with a racy wit and turn of phrase. Internationally known leprologist. Wide interests - painting, photography, bird watching (wrote a book about Malaysian birds), sailing and shooting. Died 1986 after surviving for four years after a massive stroke which left him wheelchair bound. Our father was a charismatic man with many friends, widely respected and from accounts of the prison camps, one of the outstanding figures. As far as I know he was faithful to my mother although never good at expressing easy affection.

My mother had a very difficult time when she was pregnant with Sheila. I am two years older. My parents were upcountry in Malaya when she got pregnant for the second time and almost immediately my father got typhus and very nearly died. The sister on the ward warned my mother that he might not make it. Whilst he was still convalescing from this the Japanese invasion of the Malay Peninsular started and my mother and I fled south. My father stayed at his post at the hospital as they were expecting casualties from the front line. My mother drove a group of women and children down to Singapore. My father managed to join us briefly before putting us on what turned out to be the last ship to leave Singapore before it fell. We were bombed and strafed on the way to the docks and my parents hid in the monsoon drains, covering me with their bodies whilst the Japanese planes flew over.

My father stayed behind. He went up the East Coast of Malaya hoping to link up with resistance fighters in the Cameron Highlands, but was captured and brought back to Changi where he remained for the rest of the war. I think this was in March 1942. He never spoke much about this part of his life to us, even to my mother, although she learnt something of what he had suffered from his sleep talking. He weighed seven stone when he was released and never forgave the Japanese.

The pregnancy continued to be a stressful one. My mother and I had to share a cabin with 16 others. She was put under pressure to disembark in South Africa. The journey to England was thought to be too dangerous because of the U-boats. However, she had no money and no contacts in SA and decided she must take the risk and get home to her parents.

Sheila was born six weeks after our arrival in the UK. My mother only ever talked of the difficulties she had with my birth so I suspect Sheila's was easier. I can remember Sheila soon after her birth.

We moved to St Albans to be with my mother's elder sister who had three children. This meant there were five children under five in the house. My uncle, another doctor, was away fighting in France. My mother had no idea whether my father was alive. She only had one postcard from him the whole of his imprisonment. I can remember the chaos and worries of a series of childhood illnesses. There were tensions between the sisters and my mother found this a difficult time. Sheila was breast-fed.

I am not sure how long it was before my mother found a cottage to rent, but I think we moved there when Sheila was about a year old and I was three. We led a very free life playing with the local children in the woods and being played with by Joan, the 16 year old daughter of our landlady who lived in the manor house across the road. Sheila was never a very easy child. I am placid by temperament, she rebellious. The photographs of us taken at that time by Joan reflect this; Sheila's face is full of expression and mischief. I remember elderly relatives of my father's who had come to visit, being shocked by how wilful she was. I look back on this as a happy period. Our lives were restricted by the war but as young children this did not impinge on us. My mother talked to us about our father; showed us his photograph, but I know from talking to her in later years that she often wondered if he was still alive.

My father returned in 1945 when I was five and Sheila was three. We were sent to stay across the road with Joan and her mother for a fortnight. I know this period is burnt into Sheila's mind as a terrible rejection. She talked to me recently about it during her illness. It was a hugely important event. I can still feel the banister under my hands as I looked down the stairs for the first time at the gaunt, bearded figure – so different from his photographs – so evidently overwhelmed by the children he suddenly found himself faced by. Sheila remembers crying at the garden gate at not being allowed to join them in the cottage. Recently, during her illness, Sheila expressed huge rage to me that this had been done to us. I said that I thought that either of us faced with our

Jenifer

husbands returning after years in prison would have done exactly the same to our children. The fact that we were only sent across the road and to dearly loved friends seemed to me a kindness. I said to her that our parents must have desperately needed that brief space to get to know each other again, to come to some sort of accommodation about what had happened to him and to try and plan their life together. Sheila said that she could recognise this but that her 'three year old self' still felt as bitter about this rejection as ever.

Sheila and I shared a bedroom in the cottage. Our father's presence did change our lives. He was probably more at ease with me than with Sheila simply because I was 'easier'. I did as I was told, she always bucked authority and he expected to be obeyed. I was certainly a little afraid of him and I think Sheila was too. He was an impatient man and I do not think that his time as a prisoner had made him tolerant of small children's noise and demands. He did not hesitate to smack us if annoyed.

I am aware that since her illness Sheila has felt she was sexually abused by my father at this age. I can only say that this is the first I have ever heard of it. I find it difficult to imagine when it could have happened. We were always together. We shared a bedroom. I know she did not know what a naked man looked like, as we were both curious and I remember discussing with her how we might manage to see our father naked. He never undressed in front of us and I never saw him naked until I helped nurse him in his last illness. He was not a very tactile person and rarely gave us anything more than a goodbye kiss or a brief hug on going to bed. He never made any remotely sexual gesture to me.

Sheila was a great talker and would tell me at length whom she liked and did not like. I remember my mother quoting with amusement Sheila's comment soon after my father's return that she preferred him in his photos because she had to do as she was told now. She never talked to me at all about any abuse or showed any fear of my father that was different or greater than mine. She was extraverted about her feelings and this made her attractive to be with. She would say far more about what she wanted, felt and liked than I did and was much more definite in her likes and dislikes.

My mother became pregnant with my brother Patrick who was born in 1946. Miette, a Belgian au pair, came to live with us to help. She is still a friend of the family and years later when she was staying with my parents Sheila asked her whether she had been particularly naughty as a child, (I think she felt at this stage that the family might have scapegoated her). Miette immediately answered 'Oh yes you were dreadful, amusing but dreadful!' This also meant the presence of an extra adult in the tiny cottage whose sole job it was to look after us. Before my brother's birth my father returned to Malaya to take up a post as superintendent of the Sungei Buloh Leprosarium. We followed some months later by ship.

We arrived in Malaya at the start of the Communist Emergency. The

Leprosarium was surrounded by jungle and we, together with many other expatriate children were sent off to boarding school in the Cameron Highlands. A woman who had been a POW with my father ran the school. Sheila was four and I was six when we started but my mother's twin sister Peggy was also a teacher at the school. The 'babies' school to which Sheila went was across a little valley from the main school where I was, so I did not see her in term time until she was five and moved up to the big school. This was the first time we had been parted. I feel that six was an agonisingly young age to send a child away from home but for a child of four as Sheila was it seems an extraordinary decision. My parents were in many ways still in the mould of the old servants of the Empire – personal feelings and family came after ones duty to God and Country. Indicative of this is that years later when I got married and it was easy to fly back from Africa where they then were and they could have afforded it, they were still so stuck in the attitude that you just gritted your teeth and had to miss these things, that they did not come. My mother subsequently realised how ridiculous it was and regretted it bitterly.

We were sent to boarding school in England aged eight and ten. We spent the holidays with my mother's brother Bill and his wife Pen and we only saw our parents every year or two for a summer holiday.

At school Sheila was often in trouble as she disliked authority. Despite her evident intelligence she got bad reports as she did not work at lessons until her mid-teens.

Jenifer Rohde 05.08.1993

2nd October 2002

The above notes were written for Sheila's psychiatric team. I never imagined they might be published. I have asked Sheila to restore them to their original form. Some of her editorial changes have altered the sense of what I wrote at the time. I feel that, just as contemporary medical notes should not be changed, neither should these notes, as they are what the team had to hand at the time.

Sheila gave me her book to read a week ago. It is an extraordinary and unique book. I was very moved and I find her courage in writing it wholly admirable but I do not think she is being honest about the leading factors in her adult life which might have been causal in her breakdown. I think it very unlikely that my father sexually abused her. Sheila had strange ideas at the time of her illness and, by her own admission, delusions by which she is now embarrassed. She did not always recognise me and often called me "Pat". I was also Ursa Major. Peter Rabbit and zips were of great importance to her. Communication with her whilst she was ill was very difficult, she was very inaccessible.

Now nearly ten years later I write again with the same reluctance as last time. My chief anxiety has always been that in questioning Sheila's allegation about my father, I might drive her again into her madness. I can see the allegation of abuse answers questions for her and provides a "reason" for her breakdown. However, as I said in my previous notes we neither of us knew what a naked male looked like and we were curious. I have read these notes again and stand by everything I said then, however I find I did not detail in those notes that my memory about this is specific. It was not just a generalised childhood memory of curiosity. We would have been about six and four – both of our birthdays are in June. It was a hot summer day and we were playing in the back garden of the cottage. The cottage was tiny and the bathroom was built out at the back, a single storey behind the kitchen. There was a window with a frosted fixed pane and a clear opening light at the top. We became aware that our father was having a bath. The clear part of the window was too far up for us to see in so we discussed climbing on something in order to have a look and satisfy our curiosity. At this point it became clear that Dad could hear us and he gave one of his inimitable roars of disapproval. We ran and hid. He never referred to the incident or punished us later, although we probably expected this as we were afraid of him.

I am very shocked by Sheila's additional reasoning, which I had not heard before I read this book, that our mother then colluded with this abuse by employing an au pair and then reorganising her twin sister's life so that she came to live with us....All I can say is rubbish! Miette came because our mother was expecting what turned out to be our brother Pat – born in October 1946 and Peggy our aunt came to Malaya because that was where she could find work. It suggests extraordinary powers of persuasion on my mother's part to disrupt her sister's life to that extent.

I am not prepared to let my parents' reputation be ruined by a delusion, experienced in the height of an acute psychiatric episode. They are both dead, they cannot defend themselves now, but I can and will.

I am not defending our childhood. It was enough to scar anyone. We were sent to boarding school far too early aged six and four. Aged ten and eight we were then taken home to England to school 7,000 miles away from home. We saw our parents when we flew out to Malaya (a four day journey on our own) for one summer holiday in two years. I remember weeping on my way to the airport and Sheila asking Mum why I was crying. I did not allow my mother to answer but said angrily that I was sad to be leaving the dogs! Then, in the year they were home on leave for six months, which happened every three years there were two holidays. This was almost worse because we knew they were in England but we were not with them. When I talk of it today people look at me in disbelief and shock. As I write of these things it makes me weep. My brothers, too, went through this childhood. It left all of us vulnerable.

I was moved by the account of the nurse who had been trained by Sheila and who had moved from general to psychiatric nursing, and found herself

Peter and Jenifer

nursing Sheila. She explains that whereas in physical nursing thanks and acknowledgement of the work done is given to nurses, this is rare in the psychiatric setting. I commented on this to Peter, my husband and a consultant psychiatrist. He said quietly "Yes, she is right."

I know much of psychiatry inevitably has to be done on a trial basis as tests for particular forms of psychiatric illness are not yet available, but among the treatments may be one that will work, for the patient and be literally lifesaving. I remember Peter visiting a psychiatric 'hospital' in the Philippines in the 1960s. He came back shaken to the core by what he had seen. There was no money for drugs, no money for psychotherapy, scarcely any money for staff. Patients were herded together. 'Some of our drugs and treatments may have side effects' he said 'but they are as nothing to the effects of untreated mental illness'.

I would like to record formally my thanks to this team who helped my sister when her behaviour was at its most extreme and at times difficult. It saddens me that in this book they have not been thanked by anyone else. They managed not to section her, recognising that this would have a devastating effect on her life. They took responsibility for Sheila twice when her family could no longer cope. When I visited Sheila in hospital at the height of her distress I was exhausted after half an hour and reduced to tears. I could not have coped with her although I have nursed other members of the family and through psychiatric illness. I am grateful to them for looking after her, helping her towards recovery and for giving me back a sister I can communicate with again in all her courage and complexity.

I once said to Sheila that in life I feel that I am a collaborator and that she is, and always has been, the resistance fighter. This is a resistance fighter's book. For me it would have more value if she could acknowledge that her "memory" of what my father did might have been part of her delusional system and that there were enormous stresses in her adult life at that time which are not mentioned in the book.

Jenifer Rohde 02.10.2002

12. PETER'S VIEW

I am Sheila's brother in law and second cousin. I married Jenifer when she was 20 and Sheila was 18. My mother and David, Sheila and Jenifer's father, were first cousins and had a close relationship. I am a retired consultant psychiatrist and worked for many years in the NHS and later in private practice as a general psychiatrist with a particular interest in psychotherapy.

I have seen Sheila's book for the first time this week and found it a powerful and deeply moving account of her psychotic breakdown, its effect on her and those around her and her attempts to make sense of it all. I think it is brave and forthright and yet, I think the story is incomplete and may do grave injustice to her dead father, David, a man loved and revered by many people in many countries.

We came back from a month's holiday abroad at the end of May 1993. When we got in touch, Jeremy said that Sheila was having some sort of a breakdown. I went down to Taunton on 2nd June 1993 and found her in a very disturbed state. It was that day that she was admitted to hospital. Jeremy and Rachel have described the early stages of the illness. The other graphic accounts in the book show different perspectives on her disturbed thought, talk and behaviour. Jenifer and I visited both Sheila and Obridge House as often as we could in the next weeks.

Early in her illness we heard that Sheila had said that she had been sexually abused by her father at three and a half, soon after David had returned from POW camp. It was after this that Jenifer wrote her account of their early childhood for the medical team looking after Sheila.

After a stormy course, Sheila's illness gradually improved with a great deal of help, love and care from family, friends and professionals. She was able to progress from inpatient to the community and finally come off medicines and resume her life. But, as Maggie has documented in her chapter, the belief that she had been abused by her father at three and a half, had waxed and waned but then became fixed and is the core of Sheila's own contributions to this book.

As Maggie puts it 'As her recollections became more ordered, so the consistent threads of her delusions became decipherable. The appraisal of their significance released buried memories from her childhood and she recognised that her madness was the dark side of disturbing incidents, which she had successfully repressed for nearly 50 years. This was a painful process for Sheila, whose journey back to sanity demanded that she acknowledge the abuse of her childhood and reframe her perception of her primary relationships, but also for relatives who resist her rereading of the past. However, the recognition that a suppressed and disturbing reality underlay the psychosis of the last months ultimately freed up the healing process; if there was a reason behind her experience, recovery was attainable. Her recognition empowered Sheila and she planned to return to work.' This paragraph by a close friend and observer seems to me to sum up one of the main messages of the book.

But the real question is "Is it true?" After this comes the secondary question "Does it matter whether it is true or not?"

To answer the second question first.

An untrue idea in the head is no problem to anyone else but once it is communicated or acted on it may cause difficulties for others. The knowledge of Sheila's belief that she was abused as a child has already caused distress to the members of my family who know of it. Publication of such an accusation will cause grave distress to the many people who knew David. He may be dead, but he is well remembered by many people worldwide.

This book refers in several places to alternative truths. That there should be alternative views of the same events is useful, but I wonder if it would be better described as alternative perceptions. There are moving alternative perceptions or points of view in this book. I think particularly of the family's reservations concerning the closed ward, Park View, and the view from the staff provided by Vicki [Chapter 13]. Where we come to truth in the sense of "the fact or facts; the actual state of the case; the matter or circumstance as it really is" [OED 12a] I feel there is no room for alternative truths where damage to others is concerned.

Sheila has made clear her main attitude to truth in the quote from Jung on page 47, Chapter 5 and on her dedication page.

"I can only make direct statements, only 'tell stories'. Whether or not the stories are 'true' is not the problem. The only question is whether what I tell is my fable, my truth."

She goes on to say "This would express for me my own stance when I tell of my own childhood experiences."

But she also has a secondary attitude to truth, perhaps coming from Sheila the professional who recognises a duty to others. This is expressed at the top of the third page of Chapter 6. Shakespeare, madness and myself.

"Carers need to be very secure in their own grasp of reality and to run the risk of increasing the sufferer's sense of confusion is not a kindness."

Sheila's and Maggie's chapters effectively accuse David of a criminal offence for which, if convicted now, he would serve a prison sentence and be placed on the Register of Sexual Offenders. The professional and social consequences of such a court case, even if he were cleared, do not bear thinking about. From their accounts in this book, I do not feel either Sheila or Maggie have grasped the need for "truth" to be tested against reality before it is moved from the private to the public domain. I can only assume this is because they have profoundly underestimated the effect of publication on other people.

The standard of proof for a criminal offence is "beyond reasonable doubt". This brings me back to the first question "Is it true that David sexually abused Sheila when she was three and a half years old?"

When I first heard of Sheila's allegation of sexual abuse she was in a highly abnormal mental state with many other apparent delusions – as well documented in various places in this book. Nonetheless Jenifer and I took the allegation very seriously and together, went over in detail Sheila's account and Jenifer's memory of the same period. Jenifer has discussed this in her two contributions. She concluded that it was very unlikely. She also said that she thought Sheila had remembered the layout of the house wrongly and this was relevant to the story. I suggested that we go to St Albans to look for the house and check, but Jenifer felt this was unnecessary as she felt clear in her memory. She has unusually good memory for early for early events, she can recall a verifiable incident at the age of two. She said that David had never, ever, at any time done anything remotely sexual towards her.

Jenifer checked with our daughter Kate, now in her late 30s. Kate was very close to her grandfather and had stayed with Ro and David without us. Kate had never had any sexual approach and was deeply shocked by the suggestion that her grandfather might be accused of such a thing. She was in the habit of getting into bed with Ro and David in the mornings and recalled that Ro often went off to make tea leaving her and David in bed together. This trust of David by Ro suggests that she had no concerns about her husband being left with a vulnerable young girl. It would seem to be evidence against Sheila's secondary thesis that Ro was aware of the "abuse" and took steps to keep David away from her daughters.

This negative testimony from my wife and daughter seems to me to be more credible than an idea or belief that came to Sheila when she was in the middle of an acute psychotic episode. That Sheila had hallucinations [a perception without an object] and delusions [false beliefs, not explained by the individual's culture], is well documented in the book, but when she developed the beliefs about David is not clear. The first evidence that I can find is of a phone call that Sheila made on the 27th May '93 to her aunt Daph. I understand from Daph's daughter, Anne, that she made the allegation on that day. Sheila herself, when discussing the matter with Jenifer and I on 21st September 1997, made it clear that "this came out during her illness not during her psychotherapy" [extract from my contemporary diary note. I have kept a typed diary on and off for the last fifteen years.]

The fact that the ideas about early sexual abuse did not emerge during psychotherapy or indeed during the talks about fathers mentioned on the first page of "Black Dog - Maggie's account," but during an acute psychosis, makes them, for me, less believable.

I discussed with Jenifer, Maggie's references to "The incidents in Ghana with her father when she was around 19" and "incidents that struck me as sexually abusive, although Sheila never made this interpretation her own." Her recollection is that when Sheila came back from a holiday staying alone with her father, she had described that when they both were having a siesta in the middle of the day, David had suggested that she came lay down on his bed with him rather than go off to the guest bungalow which was some way from the house. Sheila had described how this made her feel uncomfortable and intruded on but had clearly stated to Jenifer at the time, that there was no inappropriate physical contact. I can see why this might be perceived as intrusive if the invitation was unwelcome but difficult to refuse, but if my information is correct, it does not seem to constitute sexual abuse.

The lack of any approach to Jenifer during childhood seems a powerful argument against early abuse. Abusers who are sexually attracted to children notoriously transfer their attention to siblings. Both sisters would agree that Jenifer, at least as a child, was the easier and more malleable of the two and might be expected to be more co-operative. This however presupposes that David was sexually attracted to young girls. The available evidence suggests that he was attracted to adult women and I know of no corroborative evidence suggesting any sexual attraction to young children.

So, is it true that David sexually abused Sheila as a child?

Taking all the evidence available to me I have to say that the balance of probabilities is that he did not. Taking the sterner legal test of "proved beyond reasonable doubt" the answer is more emphatically "not guilty"

He is a man who had tragedy in his youth with the loss of his father, almost unendurable privation during the Japanese occupation and yet survived to have a family of fine individuals and to make a contribution to medicine that earned him world wide recognition. He does not deserve this posthumous slur.

I have been very critical of the possibility of childhood sexual abuse. I am also aware that I have attacked the main way in which Sheila [and Maggie] made sense of the psychosis. Maggie described in the extract I have quoted above how this process helped recovery. Sheila heads chapter "Memory in Madness - Repressed or False" with a question mark and ends with the words "that's enough about the possible roots of your psychosis…." These two lines enclose a letter to herself that seems to indicate little room for doubt about the reality of her "memory".

I think I should now offer an alternative view. I am doing this as a loving member of the family rather than a professional. I saw Sheila on the day she was admitted and Jenifer and I visited her and the rest of the family as often as we could. I was involved in discussions with both the family and the medical team from time to time and had time to form my own views of the developing illness. I had no access to the notes and so what I am going to say is based on what I have been told, what I have read in this book and what I have observed during the illness and over the years before and after.

I had no professional involvement with Sheila but inevitably my views are coloured by my own professional experience. I have worked in a wide variety of professional settings and while at the Maudsley hospital I worked in the psychotherapy department, either full or part-time for four years. I was a consultant general psychiatrist for over 17 years at St Mary Abbotts hospital in Kensington and after that did 10 years of part time private practice doing mainly short term psychotherapy and giving opinions on a wide variety of problems. While in the NHS I attended groups for inpatients and day patients at least a couple of times a week. In addition, I set up and always attended an evening "drop in" group at which anyone, patient, relative or carer could turn up and discuss any concerns over a cup of tea. I mention all this to indicate that I am not only familiar with a wide variety of mental problems but also discussing those problems whenever the patient, client or carer, wished.

By any standards, Sheila was very disturbed at times during her illness and needed to be in hospital despite the truly heroic efforts of her family. All the accounts and my own observations suggest she was a difficult problem for the ward staff. Vicki has given a moving account of the often thankless task they face.

I have no quarrel with Dr Ahmed's diagnosis and his summary as far as it goes, but it does not address the issues of what caused the illness. There is much more family history of mental illness, particularly depression, than Dr Ahmed mentions or perhaps knows. This does **not** mean that any one member of the family is going to get a mental illness, but it does mean that a predisposition is there **if** exceptional environmental stresses are present.

During the few months prior to her admission to hospital Sheila was under considerable stress and experienced exceptional life events. Some of these are mentioned in the accounts in the book but some are not. It is recognised that there is an association between life events and the onset of psychosis even if the symptoms do not appear to point to the influence of the event. I would like to list some of the factors and events that I think had, together, put unbearable stresses on Sheila and precipitated her breakdown.

The list is not in order of importance.

Deaths on the ward. Two are mentioned in the book a family man whose wife appeals to Sheila to help break the news to her children. Routine perhaps for a ward sister but a reminder of the stresses that go with the job. The second death is far from routine, a death during an injection followed by an investigation. I know from what Sheila said to Jenifer and myself at the time, that this was very stressful. The shock of an unexpected death during a procedure, however correctly carried out, is very traumatic. The inevitable inquiry adds further stress and self examination however clear the professional conscience is. I have seen professionals who have broken down under this stress alone.

Taking on an extra commitment to do a PhD. Ward staff start to notice the strain [see Sue Bowan's account]. Maggie in her account, recognises that she was highly stressed at this time and refers to Sheila being "in overdrive" "fitting an eight day life into a seven day week"

These are all stresses in the workplace and might be weathered without problems by most staff provided they were reasonably well supported at home. However at this time Sheila was under or was about to be under exceptional stresses at home.

The Menopause and its shadow. This is mentioned in the book. It is a risk factor for mental illness.

"the need for a hysterectomy" see Maggie's account page 168.

Ben her son was about to be 21 and was planning to go to America for three months during his long vacation, to see his US girlfriend. He is her only son. Sheila had said to Jenifer at this time that she felt this long vac indicated that she might lose Ben to America later.

There were two other major personal life events during the year or so before her illness. Both concerned members of her immediate family and were deeply disturbing to Sheila. Both caused the relevant member of family to express concern that the events had contributed to the psychosis. To protect third parties I am not giving details but I regard them both as highly significant, severe, stresses.

In my opinion the combination of all these exceptional stresses, with a possible family predisposition, is sufficient to account for Sheila's psychosis occurring at that time.

There remains the problem of why the ideas of sexual abuse by David arose and why they remained after other delusional ideas had faded.

In psychotic illness the sufferer has a tendency to lose touch with reality. Internal thought and ideas become confused with external perceptions. There is also abnormal feeling of certainty at some times. The combination of an idea with this unjustified feeling of certainty means an idea becomes fixed and a delusion [false belief] is born. In affective, that is mood disorders, delusions occur but they tend to be congruent with the mood. Thus depressives have gloomy, self denigratory delusions while in the elation of hypomania delusions are often grandiose and Sheila had those when she thought she was directing events. The other feature of hypomania is that thought is speeded up and ideas crowd into the head. At the same time there may be a conviction that the ideas are right. If this conviction persists delusions are formed.

I suspect Sheila's mind was buzzing as a result of all her stresses and ideas were flooding into her head so fast that she could not or did not have time to sort out which were real; I think the phone call to Aunt Daph was an attempt to "reality test" one of these ideas, namely that she had been abused by her father.

It is agreed by all that she had always had a highly ambivalent relationship with him and it is quite a small step for some one who has spent several years in psychotherapy and is used to thinking about themselves, to think about abuse as a possibility. Given the highly abnormal psychotic state it is also not a large step to have the feeling of certainty that is true. I think it was and is an attractive belief for Sheila to hold because it offers an explanation for so much of her feelings.

I suspect this is also the explanation for the fact that this "conviction" survived when others faded as she recovered. It serves a useful explanatory purpose in terms of coming to terms with her feeling about herself and her childhood. This is after all, one of the principal reasons for her's and everyone else's, psychotherapy.

I have always [perhaps mindful of the "need to be very secure in [my] own grasp of reality"] told Sheila that on balance I feel she is mistaken about sexual abuse by her father. We, Jenifer and I, told her gently while she was ill and in her early recovery phase. When a year or two later, I heard that she was being more public about her beliefs, I made a special journey to Taunton, to say rather more robustly to Sheila and Jeremy that we did not agree with what she was saying about her father.

On 21st September 1997 Sheila told Jenifer and me that she was planning to write about "her madness". We had a conversation with Jeremy present in which our views as put forward in this book and in Jenifer's and my papers were mirrored. On the issue of David there was little meeting of minds but I am eternally grateful to Sheila for her commitment given at that meeting, that nothing would be published without Jenifer and I having a chance to see and comment. Since then we had no significant discussions about the subject until October 2002.

I would like to end as I started by saying that I found the book deeply moving both for Sheila's honesty about her viewpoint and struggle to make sense of her illness and for the heroic way in which her family dealt with the challenge they faced.

Peter Rohde 4th October 2002

13. THE PROFESSIONAL VIEW

A psychiatric summary on Mrs Sheila Harvey from Dr W. Ahmed

Mrs Sheila Harvey was admitted to Tone Vale Hospital on the first occasion on the 2 June 1993 and discharged on the 22 July 1993.

She presented with a two-week history of being disinhibited, having an increased rate of talk and having an expansive mood. There were important stressful events at that time including pressures at work. She worked as a sister on Ward 7 at Musgrove General Hospital and there had been a reduction in the number of trained staff. There was a recent report after a cardiac arrest followed by death on the ward, where both medical and nursing interventions were questioned. She was also completing an MPhil looking at 'The role of anxiety in patients suffering from chronic breathlessness'. In addition she reported experiencing flashbacks to her own childhood concerning sexual abuse at the hands of her father.

There was no formal psychiatric history in her family, although her sister did report that her paternal grandfather had committed suicide. At the time of admission Mrs Sheila Harvey was also undergoing private psychotherapy from a therapist in Bath[1].

In her family history, her mother died in 1989. She was described, by her sister Jenifer, as a calm person who coped and was in the shadow of Mrs Sheila Harvey's father. She shared her husband's interests in sport and ornithology. He was the son of an Indian Army officer, his wide interests included photography; he wrote a book on Malayan birds and enjoyed sailing and shooting. He was internationally renowned for his knowledge of leprosy. He died in 1986 after a stroke four years previously. He was described as a charismatic man who was widely respected. He did not express affection easily. He was captured in Malaya by the Japanese and imprisoned in a Japanese prisoner of war camp in 1942 until 1945. He never forgave the Japanese for his experience during these years.

Mrs Harvey has an older sister Jenifer and two younger brothers, Patrick who was born just after the war and Simon nine years after him. Her early months were spent in St. Albans with her mother and her sister, who had three young children of her own. Then her mother moved to live in a cottage in Serge Hill, near St. Albans. Her father returned in 1945 and I gather Sheila and her sister

---

[1] I had ended weekly psychotherapy in 1986, 7 years earlier, only keeping in touch with my psychotherapist 6 monthly, Ed.

were sent to stay with the landlady and her daughter Joan across the road. Sheila felt rejected by her father. Her sister found it difficult to understand Sheila's subsequent account of her being sexually abused by her father. After Patrick's birth in 1946 the family was posted back to Malaya. Initially Sheila and her sister went to a boarding school in Malaya and subsequently both Sheila and her sister were sent back to England, again to be boarded.

On Mental State Examination during this admission, she was extremely disturbed. Initially she was dishevelled and disinhibited. Her affect was one of elation and irritability.

After that same interview she raced up and down the corridor saying loudly 'blue eyed bear, blue eyed bear lie down'. She then hit another patient several times who was quietly watching television and did not retaliate. She required heavy sedation with droperidol and minor tranquillisers, e.g. Lorazepam. During the same week she continued to be disinhibited, was incontinent of faeces and was declining to eat. Her speech showed clang associations and punning. At times she was tearful and her thoughts were increased in rate. By week three she continued to be disturbed, largely with symptoms consistent with hypomania.

By June 18th she seemed to have improved, appeared more relaxed and she decided she did not want to stay another night at Park View where she was. However, she still did not have the ability to stay to the point in her thinking and speech. Her relative improvement was short-lived and within twenty-four hours she had deteriorated once more. Her mood became elevated and she became disinhibited once more.

On June 27th she threw a book twice at another patient and she needed to be restrained. By the beginning of July she was treated with Clopixol Acuphase (Zuclopenthixol Acetate)[1] and she had gradually settled. By July 18th she was beginning to be much calmer, her mental state had improved and seemed to have remained stable.

It was clear that the above picture was consistent with an affective disorder, manic type. There was some discussion as to whether this was a disassociative state or a psychogenic psychosis. However, the timescale for both a disassociative state and a psychogenic state would be short and her disturbed periods lasted a number of weeks.

It was therefore felt that she was suffering from a bipolar affective disorder, presenting largely with manic features, although there were also some depressive features. She was finally discharged on Droperidol, 20mg three times a day and Procyclidine, 10mg three times a day.

Unfortunately, she was then re-admitted on August 18th 1993, for the second time and was discharged on October 29th. On this occasion she had become very demanding and disruptive. Whilst on Portia Ward[2] she had started to throw

---

[1] There is no record of this particular prescription in the notes. It is an antipsychotic drug used in the short-term management of acute psychosis, mania, or exacerbations of chronic psychosis. It can only be given by a deep intra-muscular injection.

[2] I had been transferred back to Park View almost immediately and was not admitted to the rehabilitation ward again until this phase of behaviour was over, Ed.

herself on the floor and against the radiator, shouting, screaming and crying when approached. When lying on the floor she would say 'I am very ill, completely bonkers, raving'. Her thoughts were bizarre. She was deliberately bruising herself as a result of her desire to punish herself. She said 'I have done many awful things – I have kissed my father, who was a mystery to me, when I was three and a half – he was a Japanese prisoner of war'. She had periods of over activity; she was restless; she was doing somersaults in the corridor and singing out loud.

She was initially treated with Chlorpromazine and this was later changed to Droperidol. She was also started on Lithium, this seemed to gradually help her and she settled, although there were periods when she was elated and also depressed for short periods. She was finally discharged on Wednesday, October 29th, with an arrangement to visit Ivor House from time to time for day care and further monitoring of her mental state.

By the summer of 1994 she had returned to work and her mental state had remained stable. She was also seeing her psychotherapist[1] which she found helpful. She continued with her regime, tailing off all remaining drugs except Lithium and by May 1996 she expressed the view that she wished to come off this drug as well. This was agreed, albeit reluctantly, on the basis that we could monitor Sheila in outpatients and re-start treatment quickly, should it prove necessary.

My view concerning Mrs Harvey's presentation is that she was suffering from a bipolar affective disorder, hypomanic type[2], which is consistent with the symptoms that she presented with.

---

[1] I only visited her on a very occasional basis. We did not re-establish regular sessions, Ed.

[2] Bi-Polar Affective Disorder - A disorder of mood (depression or elation) characterised by cyclical mood changes, occurring episodically during the course of illness. When in the depressed phase individuals present with low mood, with disturbances in physical, social and psychological well being. When manic, there is an elation or irritable mood, which has a direct effect on social and psychological aspects of the individual. Often insight into the illness is lost, some people may not recover to their previous level of functioning. Dr W. Ahmed.

Dr. Brian A. Kidd, Consultant Psychiatrist:
His Account

Introduction

This record has been produced some nine years after the event. It was strange to receive Sheila's letter in my in-tray, from a place hundreds of miles away and after all this time. It has reminded me that in the world of psychiatry we often don't hear what has become of the many people we interact with during their own crises and, trying to recall the story from my perspective as best I can, I realise that we are often surprised when patients do well and rebuild their lives.

Sheila has sent me my own notes or letters, which she could find in her records. Unfortunately these don't give as comprehensive a view of her case as I had hoped (notwithstanding the writing) and I am forced to rely on my memories to fill in the gaps. Inevitably this composite will contain inaccuracies around some of the facts but I aim to capture my impressions during the short time I worked with Sheila. I also hope to give some insight into how the psychiatrist tries to balance knowledge of biological, psychological and social elements of a person's story in a flawed process, which aims to deliver the best outcome he can.

The illness - first meeting

I recall meeting Sheila early on in my time as a Psychiatric Senior Registrar at Tone Vale Hospital in Somerset. I had completed my basic psychiatric training in Glasgow and passed my MRCPsych examinations in the winter of 1992. I had moved to the South West to broaden my experience, having previously worked only in Scotland - initially as a GP trainee and then as a career psychiatrist. A brief spell of a few months in Exeter had seen me settle into the Senior Registrar role (essentially that of an apprentice consultant) and the Tone Vale/Taunton job was my first one year post. I was attached to Dr Wakar Ahmed, a general psychiatrist and had duties in the hospital and community services - including Ivor House in Taunton, working closely with the Community Psychiatric Nurses and Ivor House staff.

As part of an early ward round (in July 1993) Dr Ahmed took me to Park View ward - the IPCU (Intensive Psychiatric Care Unit or locked ward) in Tone Vale Hospital. Sheila was one of his patients there. Our first interaction - in the corridor at the front door - made it clear to me that something was seriously wrong.

Sheila was very agitated and distressed, dressed in barely decent loose-fitting nightclothes and a large straw hat. She was clearly over-sedated but was under considerable pressure and was fighting this medication with a strong psychomotor drive. Staff were trying to guide her from the (locked) front door to allow access to the building and the result was a cross between a dance and a wrestling match - Sheila's pressure to resist jousting with the nurses' attempts to guide, then control, then restrain. She was speaking rapidly and incoherently. The sense was of distress, panic and pressure.

Sheila was finally shepherded towards her bed and we were taken to a meetings room where the ward round - an opportunity for the clinical team to discuss patients and consider their future care - took place.

We discussed Sheila's story. I have no notes to go on - the discussion would be recorded by the junior doctor - but remember being told about pressures in Sheila's family which staff felt may be important reasons for her presentation in this way. There was no significant previous or family history - often important pointers in a first presentation of a major mental illness. It was seen as important that Sheila had a background of involvement with psychotherapy - something many traditional psychiatrists and nurses are nervous of. There was also concern that she was a senior health professional. The ward staff were not sure she was actually suffering from a mental illness at all and felt there was considerable behavioural overlay in her presentation. They did acknowledge, however, that she was in receipt of considerable doses of major tranquilliser medications - medicines which in these doses would knock out a normal person. This supported the view she was under considerable psychological pressure.

Sheila was brought into the room to meet Dr. Ahmed. The meeting will have involved at least five or six professionals and my memory of this meeting is simply that Sheila was agitated and unable to talk coherently to Dr. Ahmed. Eventually the meeting ended when Sheila, appearing unhappy to leave, fell to the floor and had to be manhandled out of the room - finally grabbing onto the door and having her fingers prised from the handle before being bundled along to her room.

Diagnosis and treatment

Sheila's diagnosis was debated over the following weeks. It was clear to me that she was unwell and the degree of pressure and agitation suggested some kind of affective (mood) disorder. There continued to be a view held by some that there was considerable behavioural overlay. However, she was treated with the antipsychotic medication Droperidol in doses up to 80mg/day. I had little contact with her individually during this episode but was aware that there was a struggle trying to ensure she remained on adequate doses of medication to improve her condition without causing side effects which were too severe to tolerate. I have vague memories of some meetings involving Sheila and her husband where there was a strong wish for early discharge being resisted by worried staff. In the end, after about two months in Tone Vale, Sheila was discharged home on 22nd July with support being delivered by the CPN Ian Turner.

Relapse and recovery

I have my own records of Sheila's next admission on 18th August. I record that she "remains hypomanic and unmanageable despite Rx with Droperidol 40mg/day". My notes suggest that Sheila had taken her own discharge on 22nd July (or that the junior doctor had felt under some pressure to allow her to be discharged) and that she had had a rapid decrease in her medication over the next three weeks. Her CPN was very concerned that she was becoming hypomanic again and had requested day hospital attendance to prevent the need for admission. Her first attendance had shown her to be very agitated and pressured and ultimately she had insisted on leaving. However, after some discussions she had agreed informal admission to Tone Vale.

My own recollection of this time is vivid. As SR, I was now working almost exclusively at Ivor House. CPN Ian Turner had spoken to me about Sheila - in particular he had concerns she was becoming manic as her sleep was disrupted, she was overactive and concentrating poorly. Her husband was finding it hard to manage her at home and the sense was of impending disaster as the home supports struggled to contain her. The Ivor House day hospital idea was mooted in view of Sheila's previous desire not to be in hospital but during her time there it quickly became apparent that she was very disturbed and that admission would be necessary. I don't recall much resistance to this idea from Sheila on this occasion.

My records of the mental state examination reveal a very troubled individual demonstrating signs of both mania and depression. Contrary to her previous episode, however, I note under 'Insight' that she was "aware that (she was) ill – wants admission". The diagnosis is noted as "mixed affective state + histrionic overlay" suggesting to me that I felt Sheila was capable of exerting some control over her symptoms. I prescribed a large dose of chlorpromazine and noted we should consider working her up for lithium treatment. Lithium was initiated (according to the drug record) on 26th August.

I remember this admission as more "therapeutic". What I mean by this is that there was more of a sense of 'healing' and less of conflict. Sheila was successfully treated with major tranquillizers, antidepressants and lithium and her discharge to the community was more organised than before. She attended Ivor House after discharge and I saw her weekly to review progress and plan the withdrawal of her (substantial) medication. The aim was to reduce the medications without precipitating a relapse. I also recall taking an afternoon to go through Sheila's case notes with her to help make sense of her experiences.

I think this was a difficult but positive experience for her and this, along with discussions about the different models that psychiatrists use to try to understand the patient's experience, started to build a more positive view of this difficult time. We discussed her illness and recovery and, having a common interest in literature, found this to be a helpful vehicle to consider aspects of mental illness. Mark Vonnegut's 'The Eden Express' – a book about his own mental breakdown and recovery, written by the doctor son of the international literary figure Kurt Vonnegut – helped give some meat to our discussions.

The records show that my letters to her GP started in November 1993. By this time, she was only on 5mg of Droperidol at night. She continued on the antidepressant Prothiaden 150mg daily and lithium 1g daily. The Droperidol was stopped by the end of November and with my encouragement (really a reflection of my nervousness that we move too quickly and precipitate another episode of illness) she stayed on her antidepressants over the festive season - a period which was bound to be emotionally charged after such a difficult year. My letters start to talk of a return to work – this would prove to be the next difficult period in Sheila's recovery.

Returning to a normal life?

By the end of January Sheila was only taking lithium and her mental health was robust. The plan was to reduce the frequency of my own contact with a provisional date for discharge to the care of her GP some three months later. She was now seeing a psychologist and with his support was exploring some of the reasons for this episode of illness.

Unfortunately Sheila hit unexpected problems in April when due to return to work. I had been in discussion with the Occupational Health Doctor and had given a clear message that she was fit to return to her job. Her managers saw things differently and a period of conflict with them began. Further discussions with Occupational Health suggested that colleagues were reporting that they felt she was 'not herself' and was 'behaving strangely'. However, there was clearly no evidence of any psychiatric disorder and we could only speculate that her colleagues were seeing a change in her approach to life - a normal reaction to a 'considerable psychological experience'.

Despite my advice to the hospital management she was not permitted to return to her job as a Ward Sister and instead was appointed as a Staff Nurse. In May I was asked to give a report to the RCN regarding fitness to work and when I saw Sheila at my clinic in June she was discharged to the care of her GP with advice to monitor her lithium levels regularly to avoid any toxic effects of lithium over dosage. The report made it clear, in no uncertain terms, that I saw no reasons for restricting her return to work on psychiatric grounds. My final letter to the Occupational Health Department Doctor, in response to his enquiry as to whether or not she was 'permanently damaged' by her illness was dictated on 29th June. I refuted this interpretation of Sheila's current situation and left to take up another post on 1st July 1994.

A Psychiatrist's View

Reading my old notes and letters as well as scanning my memory banks has raised some interesting feelings about this episode of psychosis – Sheila's illness. As a shiny new psychiatrist at the time (Senior Registrars are probably at the peak of their powers in terms of being up to date with theory and practice, having just passed their Membership exams and having not [yet] been tainted by experience) she was one of the first patients I was actively involved with at a senior clinical level. Though obviously mental illness is no respecter of status or age, it is unusual to find a successful professional person presenting for the first time in her 50s and being so unwell. It raises important questions about management – which perhaps we in psychiatry are loathe to address in our normal practice – from simple things like the condition of the wards we expect people to be "healed" in to the use of medications with appalling side-effect profiles or control and restraint techniques.

On reflection I am quite proud of the work that was done with Sheila. I know that the clinical team working with her was trying hard to treat her well – but that sometimes it is hard to match what a patient needs with what they feel they need or want.

There are always lessons to learn in such human experiences, however. For me the main lesson is just how much the little things (like talking about books or respecting a person's right to question and debate my management plans or even diagnostic frameworks) make a difference to the experience a person has during a period of illness.

Nine years on and Sheila's surprise letter tells me she is well and as active as ever. It seems irrelevant to me what diagnostic label is applied to this period of distress or what theoretical framework is applied to explain its aetiology. What is more important is that a good outcome has been achieved - whether the product of medical treatment, therapeutic work or Sheila's own personal fortitude.   Brian Kidd. December 2002

Vicki's Account

I first met Sheila when I was completing my final year of general nurse training. She was a formidable lady who was awarded a great deal of respect from her team, simply because she was so proficient at her work. It seemed she knew most things about respiratory disorders and was destined to ensure all the nurses in the team were as well informed. Nursing was definitely Sheila's vocation and for me she provided an excellent role model. She was addressed as Sister Harvey by nurses and doctors alike, because that was who she was.

At this time there was a great deal of change happening. The NHS, as it was, was dissolving and becoming Trusts, the first steps toward privatisation by the Conservative Government. Sister Harvey's ward was moved from a small hospital site to the main general hospital in Taunton. This was a busy time for all the team, especially Sister Harvey, but she always seemed to have enough energy and motivation for everyone and the transition went smoothly.

I qualified whilst working on Sister Harvey's ward and left soon afterwards to take up a staff nurse post in the surgical department. After leaving I had little contact with her, just at Christmas on the ward night out. Despite having qualified and gaining more self-confidence I still found her a formidable lady, to the extent that when socialising I still referred to her as Sister Harvey.

The next time we were to meet was under very different circumstances. It was early summer 1993 and I had completed my psychiatric training and been a staff nurse at Park View, a psychiatric intensive treatment unit, for a year. A referral was received for Sheila Harvey, a sister at Musgrove Park Hospital. My stomach turned, I had no doubt it was the same Sister Harvey, although a part of me refused to believe it could be so. Initially I felt anaesthetised, for want of a better description, completely numb and devoid of feeling. However, as I began to absorb this news the emptiness was replaced by a whole array of emotions and I regarded the situation with a great deal of trepidation.

I find it quite peculiar that when faced with stressful or adverse situations I have a tendency to minimalise my thinking to a level that is safe and acceptable to me. I guess it's a coping mechanism and that day was no exception. Instead of considering the many pressing issues, such as the nature of her illness; will we be able to maintain her dignity; will we be able to maintain confidentiality (after all she was a very prominent lady within the neighbouring trust), my concern was what should I call her? Sister Harvey would have been totally inappropriate, Sheila was out of the question; it would have to be Mrs Harvey, even though that felt awkward too. I think in some ways I was secretly hoping she would not recognise me or even remember me. I was dubious as to what her response to me would be – would she feel uncomfortable with the situation as I did, would she insist I was moved to a different unit to work or maybe she had so much on her mind she wouldn't care?

I discussed my concerns at length with Maggie (the unit manager) – none of the staff were wholly comfortable with the situation. Suggestions were raised as to whether an alternative Trust or Unit would be more appropriate (as would normally occur with a member of staff). However, it was decided that Sheila would come to us and we would review the situation if difficulties (including my involvement) arose.

My colleagues recognised and accepted the added stresses I carried during Sheila's stay with us and without their support I may not have survived as well as I did.

I finished my shift before Sheila arrived and was off duty for the next couple of days. In many ways I was relieved as it meant I didn't have to face my anxieties, although I was well aware that this was only a temporary reprieve. My days off were not as relaxing as they might have been in consequence.

The situation was complicated further in that I was sharing a house with a nurse who was a member of Sister Harvey's team. She had mentioned on several occasions during the weeks prior to Sheila's admission that she had changed at work, becoming increasingly short-tempered, more irritable and intolerant. I was not surprised to hear this considering the enormous levels of stress Sheila was under, staff shortages and increased work load and I seem to recall some kind of litigation although the details of this are vague. When I heard that Sheila had 'gone off sick' with depression I really was not at all surprised, but I didn't for one minute anticipate she would be admitted to my unit.

After a stressful day my friend and I would sometimes discuss events in very general terms (never naming patients to maintain confidentiality). I was now in a situation where I could not 'offload' anxiety by discussing my predicament, however vaguely, for fear that I would breach confidentiality – or my friend would put 'two and two together'. Hence, by the time I was due to go back to work I had had time to mull things over to realise the enormity of it all and was feeling extremely apprehensive.

The shift started with a handover, the outline of Sheila's behaviours was alarming and as I sat listening to a catalogue of incidents and descriptions of somebody I couldn't recognise at all, I can remember thinking 'there but for fortune go I, or anybody here for that matter'. It suddenly became so apparent what a fine line we all tread between sanity and insanity and how fragile our lives really are. When I worked in the general hospital I would be nursing someone with lung cancer and during my break have a cigarette, safe in the knowledge it would never happen to me. Similarly I nursed people with mental health problems, not once considering it could be me; now everything had changed, my boss could become ill, my colleagues could become ill, my friends, my family - me. I was no longer immune, no longer infallible. I was potentially as vulnerable as all of my patients.

Sheila was in her side room, lying quietly on the bed. She wasn't as tall as I remembered and looked extremely tired. I recall bruising on her arms and legs, sustained when she threw herself to the floor, rolled off her bed and banged her arms on the radiator. Later we nursed her on a mattress on the floor in her room in an attempt to prevent further injury.

As I entered her room she looked up, regarded me with dark and weary eyes. 'Oh my darling, my darling!' she exclaimed in a very theatrical manner. I took it from this she remembered me, although was a little less formal than she'd been on previous occasions. I tried to make conversation, which wasn't easy as I felt awkward and Sheila didn't appear to be listening, just repeating herself. 'Oh my darling, zip, zip, zip.'[1] My presence there seemed to be exacerbating things, Sheila was obviously becoming more agitated, so I made my excuses and left.

Over the next few weeks there was very little change. Sheila had moments of lucidity, usually when her family were visiting, but more often than not they were short-lived. She wouldn't eat or drink without a great deal of encouragement, it was almost as if so much was going on in her mind that she didn't have the time. One Sunday lunch the hospital chaplain and myself sat with her in the lounge to try and encourage her to eat a bowl of ice cream, with little success. Eventually I fed her, sneaking in a spoonful between words, all the time wondering if Sister Harvey was in there, would I ever get to meet her again? I felt sad, but more than that, useless. I hadn't nursed anybody in psychiatry that I had known before. I knew Sister Harvey, but was faced with someone totally different.

Sheila was hard work for the whole team, sometimes incoherent, communicating with nods or headshakes and hand gestures. She would scream, shout and throw things around. Seeing people whose illness makes them behave in such ways is difficult for the team, with Sheila it was even harder because we knew she was a fellow professional and worried for her should she recall it when well.

My concerns regarding my presence making things more distressing for Sheila had subsided. I spent a great deal of time with her on a one-to-one basis. There were periods when she would become very anxious, distressed and difficult to reach. I would sit with her and hold her as she cried, stroke her head and wait for the mood to pass. Her distress saddened me. I felt so inadequate as it seemed there was nothing else I could do, but when she calmed and regained her composure those feelings within me subsided and I knew my worth.

There were some occasions when Sheila would enter the nursing office or lie across the floor, sometimes throwing things around and refusing to leave.

---

[1] I was dealing with the American postal zip code, for some reason. It was probably Rachel whom I was 'seeing'.

This made taking phone calls, talking to doctors, or discussing other patients' care impossible. She would not respond to verbal persuasion and would become resistive when staff attempted to escort her out, to the extent of kicking and attempting to bite staff on occasions. This ultimately resulted in her being restrained and moved to her room. She would sometimes antagonise the other patients in a similar way, taking their belongings[1], entering their rooms or throwing things at them whilst they were trying to watch television.

On one occasion Sheila was complaining about the smoky environment of the lounge; staff advised she would find a cleaner environment in her own room but she ignored this and threw a foot stool at the window instead. Staff intervened to prevent her doing it again, restrained her and removed her to her room.

From conversations I have had with Sheila during her recovery and since, she has told me how distressing being restrained was for her. Never having been in that situation I can only imagine what it must be like. As a nurse, I can say that in my experience, restraining people is one of the most traumatic and stressful aspects of my job. Consequently it is only used as a last resort. I am truly sorry Sheila experienced restraint, as I am sorry any patient has to. I recognise it is as distressing for the patient concerned as it is for the staff who are involved.

I think sometimes psychiatry is tainted by its past history with stories of abuse, beatings with wet towels, shackles, dungeons and straitjackets. Practices have changed, but unfortunately many of the presenting problems have not. Psychiatric nurses are facing an increasing barrage of violence that has to be dealt with in a caring and humane way. It is not always possible to reason with somebody who has lost touch with reality, no matter how hard one tries. When that lost reality results in violence we have a duty to protect the individual, our patients, our colleagues and ourselves and so restraint is sometimes unavoidable.

Sheila's mood was changeable, sometimes she would be warm and chatty, talking quite freely and appearing grateful for the care she was receiving. It was at these times that Sheila would go out walking with staff. She seemed to enjoy this, maybe because it gave her time away from the hustle and bustle of the unit and the smoky environment. She appeared to respond well to the undivided attention and seemed to relax more. I also enjoyed these walks, they gave me an indication that she was getting better as I caught glimpses of how she used to be – her intellect, her sensitivity and her very dry sense of humour. The grounds of Tone Vale were beautiful, with a bowling green, cricket pitch, tennis courts and a small church. There was a pleasant view of the Quantocks and a general air of tranquillity. Quite often Sheila and I would stroll to the church and sit in comfortable silence for a while.

At other times Sheila would be hostile, making hurtful and derogatory

[1] At the time I believed absolutely that these things were mine.

remarks (unjustified in my opinion) to my colleagues. I was never on the receiving end of them and so felt this was under Sheila's control. I must admit to feeling some resentment about this and disappointment in her. I had to work hard on remembering my personal feelings had no place when it came to patient care.

Nurses are often the recipients of cutting verbal abuse and sometimes physical abuse, as mentioned previously. Gratitude from patients is not often forthcoming, many believing it is our fault they are detained and that we force treatment on them as a punishment, or for our own pleasure. It is not usually until they have turned the corner to recovery that we see their attitudes change. It is not uncommon for me to leave the unit at the end of a shift feeling uptight, tired, hurt and emotionally drained. It is for this reason that the structure of the team is of such great importance.

At Park View there were 21 members of staff of varying designations. Each was an individual with different skills, personality and experience, working closely together to provide the best level of care we could offer. I believe it was this, coupled with the sheer strength and courage of Sheila and her family that enabled her to make the remarkable recovery she did.

In many ways it sounds that my job is a thankless one. When I was working in the general hospital I would invariably leave my shift feeling that I had been of some use. A lot of patients would say 'goodbye', 'thank you' or 'see you tomorrow'.

These were small tokens of gratitude that I accepted without realising their significance. Now, eight years on, I don't look for them and I certainly don't expect them. My reward come from seeing people like Sheila 'well' and knowing our efforts as a team helped this to be possible.

14. FRIENDS AND COLLEAGUES

Sue Bowen's Account

Sheila and I first met about seven years ago when she interviewed me for a Health Care Assistant's post on her ward. My first impression was that I liked her. She was obviously intelligent and astute, with a keen sense of humour. She would need one as she offered me the post.

I was pleased about this as Ward 7 was special. Nurses clamoured to gain experience there and usually wanted to return when their time was up. It was a happy place where everyone worked well together. It was also a place for learning. Sheila was a good teacher and always answered your question, no matter how stupid it might seem to the person asking. One of her talents was to make us all feel an important part of the team. I can remember clearly one thing that Sheila said to me at interview;

'There is no hierarchy on this ward. Everyone is equal. There is only one leader and that's me.'

It went something like that and it worked.

Although you had to work hard and give your all, it was always a pleasure to actually go to work, to be part of a well-organised team who worked with enthusiasm and a sense of fun.

Like a lot of things in life they creep up on you, take you unawares. Yet all the time the signs are there, which we only see on hindsight.

That's how it was with Sheila's illness. Simply one minute she was there as usual and the next gone, never to return. I think if we had known she wasn't going to come back as our ward sister it would have made it much harder for us to carry on. At the time Sheila went off (bang), it had been a very demanding time for us all, both physically and mentally - lots of immense sadness to cope with while smiling at the rest of the world.

One particular event I remember - and I know Sheila will remember it much better than myself, concerns such sadness. The patient was middle-aged, had suffered a stroke and despite all our efforts he died. His situation was that he had been married twice. He had a grown family from the first marriage and the second time had married a younger wife who had produced two lovely children, who at the time of his death were aged around three and seven. They were a loving and very caring family, the grown up and the young family getting on well together. It was clear how much they all loved this man. They visited frequently and often helped with his care.

There was such heartache and disbelief for them to deal with when he died. Sheila was always there for the family, supporting them and honestly answering all their questions. She got very involved with this lovely family. The young children weren't able to grasp what had happened to Daddy. Their Mum asked Sheila to talk to the children about their Daddy dying. I remember how difficult a task this was for her, how this was echoed in her face.

I can't pinpoint an exact time when things started to go wrong. On the surface things ticked along as usual, the job got done. The waters were beginning to have tiny ripples of dissatisfaction upon its otherwise smooth surface. They started with mutterings and murmurings of things not being quite right, totally alien to our ward. The murmurings got louder as feelings of things not being as they should be increased. Most of the staff put Sheila's distraction down to doing too much. She was doing a degree course with Exeter University. This involved a lot of research and following through patients who had been on the ward in their homes. Obviously this took a lot of time and organisation, so that the general feeling was that she took too much on.

I clearly remember Sheila's last shift. She looked pale, tired and distracted. Her eyes were vague with an 'I'm out for the day' look. The hustle and bustle of the ward was all around us. I think hospital staff have the same motto as actors, 'the show must go on'. Anyway on this particular morning I thought Sheila was in need of a break so I went and made two cups of coffee and put them ready in the staff room. She didn't argue when I told her we were going for coffee.

I don't recall anything in particular that was said. Sheila wasn't making much sense. She was letting out a few choice swear words though. She was very distressed and upset and said she couldn't face going back on the ward. It was obvious that she wasn't able to do so. I told her she was the boss and she should give herself the rest of the day off. I retrieved her bag from her office and she duly went home.

We eventually got to know how serious Sheila's illness was and with just one exception we were sympathetic and wished we could do something to help. I believe we all thought the best thing we could do was to keep our ward going until Sheila returned.

Black Dog - Maggie's account.

When we first came to Taunton in 1982, I used to meet Sheila from time to time at school functions, a tall serious woman with a powerful and attractive face. We started to be invited to the same social gatherings: I modified my views of her demeanour as I recognised an anarchic streak and a wicked sense of humour. At some point in the following spring or summer, Richard and Sally Lister came for supper and Richard regaled us with an account of their dinner party the previous weekend, when 'this woman', who was the sister of a friend of Sally's, came and argued with everyone.' The most contumacious person' he'd ever met, said Richard, 'the sort of person who'd argue black was white to provoke a response'. When it dawned on me that Sheila and Jeremy were the last week's supper guests, I resolved there and then to pursue Sheila as a friend.

We invited Sheila and Jeremy to supper with the Coes: John Coe - now there's someone else who likes to disagree on principle - and our friendship has not looked back. When Sheila went to work at Musgrove, her shifts and my part-time hours slotted together well. I remember that Thursday mornings rapidly became a time for both of us where we chewed over our lives - our relationships with our mothers (who met when we took them out for a pub lunch once near Hunthay), our children, the shifting sands of our spiritual belief and, inevitably, books. Sheila was reliably partisan when I was angry with the Health Service's inadequate addressing of Frances' chronic ear problems. I hope I was similarly there for her when her mum died so suddenly. She began a London external degree in English Literature. When one of my lumbar discs collapsed, she pitched in at exactly the right note: 'Stop lying there feeling sorry for yourself, and dredge up everything you were ever taught about Old English.' My initial response was to fire off a few words in Saxon, but we laughed so much as I struggled to come to grips with the forgotten inflexions that my head detached from the pain and gave me a breather. And Sheila explored every glory hole in our house as I racked my brain for where I had stashed the Anglo-Saxon Primer. From such does true intimacy ensue.

We talked about fathers and I realised that there were painful and unresolved issues around that had complicated her experience of ill health as an undergraduate and there were also incidents that struck me as sexually abusive, though Sheila never made this interpretation her own. Associated issues bubbled up from her psychotherapy, which I seem to recall stem from about this time.

I suppose she must have decided about a year into her English Literature degree that her real calling was to pursue research into an aspect of her nursing and it was wonderful to see someone truly fired by a project. I did worry that with her research and her job she seemed to have an eight day life to fit into a seven day week, but the harder she worked the more energy she seemed to have. I remember this being particularly so when she gave a talk about her research to a convention in London, forgot her transparencies and had to dragoon Ben into bringing them to her NOW by train.

Sheila's mortal frame was running on overdrive for months before she was ill. The autumn before, she had spoken of needing a hysterectomy, but had decided that she had not got time to sit around and do nothing for three months. She charged on at an awesome rate.

Around Easter, I remember first becoming really concerned because the ramifications of hospital restructuring to operate as a Trust seemed to dominate and intrude on everything, though I was reassured by the plans to take a walking holiday in the Auvergne at Whit. I wondered whether she was an over-wound spring, or an over-shaken pop bottle.

How did I realise she was ill? I know it all happened suddenly and very quickly. I think it began as a comment by a friend that there was some doubt about the holiday; a few days later Chris dropped in to Obridge House around lunchtime on a Saturday. Jeremy had seemed perplexed and distrait; Sheila said mystifyingly, 'But Chris, where do you fit into all this that's going on?' Days later she was in Tone Vale.

It was Pauline who told me that she was seriously ill and that visiting was being rigorously controlled. About three weeks later, Jeremy contacted me to say that I could visit and that Sheila had asked me to. All my experience as a social worker in a psychiatric setting gave me no protection from the shock of having to knock at the door of a locked ward to ask to see my dear friend. Professional knowledge of mental illness gave me no passage to navigate Sheila's psychosis. It ought to have been familiar territory, but I was in an alien land without a map.

It is hard at a distance to remember an accurate sequence. On my first visit I took raspberries from the garden, with cream and Sheila ate them with gusto. Another time I remember calling in at lunch time and massaging Sheila's feet with Chanel talc, brought by another friend; we spoke of pleasing physical experiences, bodily pleasure, soothing sensation; threading in and out of this was a fearsome story of Peter Rabbit. I remember Jo coming home and being moved beyond words to see this young woman nurturing her mother as surely as she had been nurtured herself. To my mind, Jo showed an empathy for her mother's mad self that transcended everyone else's. Of all of us, I felt that Jo had the greatest facility to use her raw vulnerable feelings to ground Sheila in the reality of her family's love for her.

The weeks went by. She missed our Silver Wedding party at the end of June. I have seen people more floridly psychotic; but I do not recall anyone so mad for so long. She first came home in mid August, I think; it was certainly around Book Club time. She was like a dustbin with its lid jammed on tight. One wondered how long it would be before it blew off again. I remember sitting upstairs reading to her one afternoon, while Sheila fought to stay rational. It was no surprise to hear that she was back in hospital. I do think, though, that there was a different feel this second time, a sense that our Sheila was fighting back, determined to get back in control, a battle she won as autumn approached.

Life is full of quirks that come upon us unawares. By the time Sheila was out of hospital with a surer grip on her life, I'd injured my back quite seriously. I was at home all day, every day. Both of us needed company. Most afternoons we went swimming. I needed the gentle supported exercise; Sheila needed occupation. She took up knitting. Helen Knott suggested chewing gum. I remember this as a time of dark circles under her eyes, teeth clenched, mouth firm. It was a time of recall, as she began to remember the experiences of the last few months. I remember the sense of sheer gutsy willpower in her determination to establish a memory of her madness until it metamorphosed into an experience that she could address with rationality.

It had been a great support to the family through the summer that Sheila's brother-in-law was a psychiatrist and I knew that Peter had been a real tower of strength in marshalling a treatment programme. Her sister Jenifer too had been an important source of information about Sheila's early years. The question of sexual abuse had been raised and robustly denied. I think this was still Sheila's belief when she came out of hospital. However, through October and November, as she talked again about her undergraduate experience of ill health and the incidents in Ghana with her father when she was around 19, she began to question this belief.

She read the medical notes; she read the nursing notes. These were perhaps the most harrowing, since they brought her face to face with the things she actually did, rather than the other accounts of observations about her rationality, but in the end, the nursing notes probably gave her more useful pegs with which to pin down her confused memory of the chronology of the summer.

As her recollections became more ordered, so the consistent threads of her delusions became decipherable. The appraisal of their significance released buried memories from her childhood and she recognised that her madness was the dark side of disturbing incidents, which she had successfully repressed for nearly 50 years. This was a painful process, not only for Sheila, whose journey back to sanity demanded that she acknowledge the abuse of her childhood and reframe her perception of her primary relationships, but also for relatives who resisted her rereading of the past. However, the recognition that a suppressed and disturbing reality underlay the psychosis of the last months ultimately freed up the healing process; if there was a reason behind her experience, recovery was attainable. Her recognition of this empowered Sheila and she planned to return to work.

The healing profession's belief in the possibility of the healing process proved to be token. Sheila was cut to the quick when she was told she would not be allowed to return to direct nursing. I remember her sobbing that it felt as if they had gouged her insides out with a spoon. As her friend, I feared that this rejection would set back, if not destroy her recovery.

I wondered, as I wrote 'recovery', whether I ought not to put it in inverted commas, for I had this feeling that while we had a sane and rational Sheila back (and God, I was grateful for that), her journey had changed her. We had lost the gutsy, anarchic, uninhibited spirit and had to settle for someone who quite looked like Sheila, but who had a slightly ponderous manner: she had lost her glee.

In the end, Musgrove found a niche for her to return to in staff training and the boost that returning to work gave her was visible. As she came off her drugs, so the personality fog lifted. The biggest change came when she came off Lithium and re-took possession of responsibility for her mood. Giving up Lithium was, I think, the keystone that actually returned Sheila back to us. That straitjacket of quiet behaviour dropped away and her wicked humour returned. It gave me such joy to witness this. Today, I see a Sheila fully restored to us, with an extra dimension of humility for the capacity of the human soul to suffer. I feel very humble when I reflect on what a stronghold she has made of the black abyss she went through.

APPENDIX – Drugs Prescribed During Admissions

Drug summary.

As required prescriptions			Given	
DROPERIDOL 2/6/93	20mg. o/im	4hrly if agitated or aggressive	2/6/93 x 1. 9pm	
3/6/93 "	10-20.o/im	"	3/6/93 'o' 20mg.7pm 4/6/93. 8.50am 'o' 10mg 8/6/93. 8.50am.10mg; 13/6/93. 9.30pm.10mg 14/6/93. 10.20pm.20mg /im 17/6/93. 11.00am.20mg/o 19/6/93. 1.25am.20mg/o 20/6/93. 8.15pm. 20mg/o 23/6/93. 10.30am. 20mg/o 24/6/93. 8.45am. 20mg/o 25/6/93. 12.50pm. 20mg/o 26/6/93. 5.pm. 20mg/o 27/6/93. 1am,7.20am,6.10pm. 20mg. 28/6/93. 10.15. 20mg	An anti-psychotic or neuroleptic drug. Generally tranquillises without causing impaired consciousness. Used to quieten disturbed patients. Recommended dose 5-20mg every 4-8 hours. Side effects:- 1)**Parkinsonian symptoms:- abnormal face/body movements, restlessness,** tardive dyskinesia. Antimuscarinic drugs (i.e Benzhexol), used to offset these effects. 2)**Hypotension** and interference with temperature regulation
2/7/93-6/7/93	20mg o/im	pm at night	6/7/93. 3.35am	
2/7/93-6/7/93	20mg o/im	4-6hrly prn	6/7/93. 11.05 pm	
6/7/93	20mg im	4 hrly as reqd for agitation		
BENZHEXOL 8/6/93	2mg.o	4 hourly – side effects	8/6/93. 4.20pm 9/6/93. 8.35am	An anti-muscarinic drug used to offset drug-induced Parkinsonism. Side effects, dry mouth, GI disturbances, **dizziness, tachycardia, hypersensitivity, nervousness, mental confusion, excitement, psychiatric disturbances (!).** These may necessitate discontinuation of treatment.
CHLORAL HYDRATE 14/6/93	0.5-1g.o	pm - insomnia	16/6/93. 11.30pm. 1g/o 21,22,23,26/6/93. Pm. 1g	Role as hypnotics now very limited. Short term use for insomnia. Side-effects: gastric irritation, abdominal distension, **vertigo, ataxia, staggering gait, rashes,headache, light headedness,, excitement, nightmares, delirium.**
THIO-RIDAZINE 14/6/93	75-100mg.o		15/6/93. 9pm. 100mg For short-term adjunctive management of agitation, violent or dangerously impulsive behaviour 75-200mg daily recommended.	An anti-psychotic drug. Similar side effects to Chlorpromazine hydrochloride – less sedating, more likely to induce **hypotension**.
PRO-CYCLIDINE 1/7/98 2/7/93	5-10mg. o/im 10mg o	prn – 4hrly. Agitation 4-6 hrly prn	1/7/93. 1.15pm. 5mg	For indications etc similar to Benzhexol hydrochloride. Used in drug-induced Parkinsonism.
PARA-CETAMOL 13/7/93	500mg – 1g o	4-6 hrly prn max 8/24	13/7/93. Md 1g	
MIST MAG TRISILICATE	10ml o	As required for heart burn		
Once only and pre-medication drugs				
Benzhexol 7/6/93	2mg. o		2.30pm	See above
Paracetamol 28/6/93	1g. o		10.35pm	
Chloral Hydrate 30/6/93 &1/7/93	2g. o 2g. o		1.15am 2.30am	See Above

APPENDIX – Drugs Prescribed During Admissions

MIST MAG TRISILICATE	10ml	oral	As required for heartburn	
LORAZAPAM 1/7/93 9/7/93	1mg. o 2mg o		13.15pm 10am	Anxiolytic. Short-term use in anxiety or insomnia, in diazepam family. Side effects: drowsiness, light headedness next day, **confusion,ataxia, amnesia, occasionally hypotension, rashes etc**

Regular prescriptions				
CYCLO-PROGYNOVA 2/6/93	1mg. o	am/21 day cycle	3/6/93. Am – restarted on 11/6/93 – 1/7/93inc. continues	Hormone Replacement Therapy.
ZOPICLONE 3/6/93	7.5mg. o	pm	3/6/93 – 9/6/93inc. pm	Hypnotic. Short-term use. Side effects: bitter or metallic taste, GI disturbances, **irritability, confusion, depressed mood; drowsiness, dizziness, incoordination, hypersensitivity, hallucinations, nightmares, behavioural disturbances - including aggression.**
DROPERIDOL 4/06/93 represcribed 1/7/93 2/7/93 –6/7/93 8/7/93 – 14/7/93 14/7/93 22/7/93	10mg. o 20mg. o 25mg o 25mg o 20mg o 20mg o	qds qds 6.00,10,2,6,10. Check to make sure not over-sedated qds qds tds	4/6/93. pm x 2 5/6/93. am.md.pm.pm. 6/6 –9/6 " 1/7/93 –2/7/93 2/7/93 pm – 6/7/93 8-14/7/93 14 – 22/7/93 22 -	See above
THIORIDAZINE 10/0/93 re-prescribed 14/6/93 " 16/6/93 " 17/6/93 " 24/6/93 " 24/6/93	75mg. o 75mg. o 100mg. o 150mg. o 150mg. o 200mg. o	bd tds tds tds md.pm.pm. am	10/6. pm 11/6 – 13/6 &14/6 am 14/6 (ref x 1) – 16/6 17/6 (ref x 1) 18/6(ref x 3) 19/6 - 24/6 inc. 24/6 – 1/7 inc. "	See above.
AMITRIPTYLINE 28/6/93	75mg. o	night	28/6 – 30/6	Tricyclic anti-depressant. Cautions – **history of mania/psychosis(may aggravate psychotic symptoms)** Side effects: rashes, **hypersensitivity, hypomania or mania, etc**
LORAZEPAM 1/7/93 Re-prescribed 2/7 –14/7/93 15//93 – 19/7/93	1mg. o 1mg. o	bd qds	Never given Make sure not over sedated	2-15/7/93 15-19/7/93
PROCYCLIDINE 1/7/93 2/7/93	10mg. o 10mg. o	Bd tds	2/7/93.am 2/7/93 –19/7/93	See Above

APPENDIX – Drugs Prescribed During Admissions

READMISSION

As required prescription			Given	
CHLOR-PROMAZINE 18/8/93 18/8/93 – 26/8/93	200mg. o 200mg. o	6-8 hrly for agitation 2 hrly for disturbed behaviour in addition to regular doses. Usual maintenance dose 75 – 300 mg daily. Up to 1G daily may be necessary.	18/8/93 at 4.15pm	Used as an anti-psychotic drug to relieve florid symptoms such as thought disorder, hallucinations and delusions and to prevent relapse. Those in acute phase usually respond better than those with chronic symptoms.. It is thought that they block the dopamine transmission in the brain. It has a marked sedating effect. Side effects – Parkinsonian effect – occasionally tardive dyskinesia; hypothermia; **drowsiness; apathy; pallor; nightmares; insomnia; depression and more rarely agitation; parasympathetic effects; rashes and many more.**
SENNA 19/8/93	2 Tabs	Nocte prn		
CHLOR-DIAZPOXIDE 19/8/93	25mg. o	4-6 hrly prn for withdrawal symptoms	60-100 mg can be given daily in divided doses.	Used in anxiety. Side effects: **drowsiness; light headedness; confusion; dependence Occasionally headache, vertigo, hypotension, salivation changes, rashes, changes in libido**,etc.
PRO-CYCLIDINE 20/8/93	5-10mg. o/im	4-6 hourly prn for EPSE (?)		
LACTULOSE 20/3/93 –26/8/93 26/8/93	5-10ml o 5-10ml o	At night prn for constipation prn		
DROPERIDOL	10-20mg.o	4-6 hrly prn for disturbed behviour		
Once only and premedication drugs				
CHLOR-PROMAZINE	200mg. o		18/8/93 2.30	
TEMAZEPAM	20mg. o		30/8/93 11.45pm	
Regular prescriptions				
CHLOR-PROMAZINE 18/8/93 – 19/8/93 19/8/93-20/8/93 20/8/93-23/8/93 23/8/93-26/8/93	200mg 200mg 200mg 100mg	tds qds qds (timings adjusted) qds	18-19/8/93 19,20/8/93 20-23/8/93 – omitted 21/8 BP down. 23-26/8/93	
PROCYCLIDINE 18/8/93-20/8/93	10mg	tds	18-20/8/93	
LORAZEPAM 18/8/93-30/8/93	2mg. o	tds	18-30/8/98	
CYCLO PROGYNOVA	1mg. o	21 day cycle 7 day break	continues	
LITHIUM CARBONATE 26/8/93 – 30/8/93 30/8/93 – 30/9/93 30/9/93 – 20/10/93 21/10/93 – discharge	400mg o 800mg o 1g o 1g	od od od od	26-29/8/93 30/8-30/9/93 30/9/93-16/10/93 21-27/10/93	Used on the prophylaxis and treatment of mania, in the prophylaxis of manic/depressive illness, in the prophylaxis of recurrent depression. In long-term use therapeutic concentrations have been thought to cause histological and functional changes in the kidney. Side effects: GI disturbances, fine tremor, polyuria and polydipsia, weight gain, progressing to increase in GI disturbance, muscle weakness, drowsiness, sluggishness, giddiness with ataxia, coarse tremor, lack of co-ordination, dysarthria and leading on to

APPENDIX – Drugs Prescribed During Admissions

				more severe effects.
DROPERIDOL 26/8/93 –22/9/93 22/9/93 – 27/9/93 22/9/93 – 27/9/93 27/9/93 – 3/10/93 27/9/93 – 29/9/93 29/9/93 – 20/10/93 3/10/93 – 7/10/93 7/10/93 – 17/10/93 21/10/93 - discharge	10mg 10mg 5mg 5mg 10mg 20mg 10mg 5mg 15mg	tds bd – md/pm am am/md night night am/md am/md night	26-22/9/93 22/9/93-27/9/93 " 28/9/93–1/10/93 27&28/9/93 29/9/93-20/10/93 3-7/10/93 7-14/10 21 & 26,27/10/93	
CHLOR- DIAZPOXIDE 9/9/93 –13/9/93 13/9/93 – 14/9/93 14/9/93 –16/9/93	15mg 10mg 10mg	qds qds tds	9-16/9/93, omitted often 13–16/9/93, some double doses apparently given i.e 25mg nocte 14th and 15th.	See above for side effects.
NYSTAN VAGINAL CREAM 10/9/93		Nocte for 2 weeks for vaginal thrush		
NYSTAN PESSARIES 10/9/93		"		
DOTHIEPIN 4/10/93 14/10/93	100mg 50mg	Nocte am	4-23/10/93 14 – 28/9/93	An anti-depressive drug used in depressive illness especially where sedation is required. A tricyclic drug. Side effects – Arrythmias and heart block (occasionally), drowsiness, dry mouth, blurred vision, constipation, urinary retention and sweating. Dosage up to150mg daly (225mg in some circs.)